Th _
EMOTIONAL
SIDE

of
SELLING
a
SMALL
BUSINESS

JAMISON WEST

The Emotional Side of Selling a Small Business

Cover and internal design by Elena Reznikova
Front cover illustration by erhui1979 (istockphoto.com, modified)

E-book ISBN: 978-1-7378360-0-1
Paperback ISBN: 978-1-7378360-1-8
Hardcover ISBN: 978-1-7378360-2-5

Jamison West
www.jamisonwest.com

To my boys, Mahlon and Xander.

Contents

Foreword

THIS BOOK TACKLES A TOPIC that people tend to ignore or gloss over. The transition that happens during the mergers and acquisitions (M&A) process is life-changing, and most entrepreneurs and founders don't prepare adequately for selling—or 'what's next.'

I've been leading and assisting small business owners for over three decades. Having founded a number of companies myself—and doing eight buy-side acquisitions and three sales—I've been on this journey multiple times. And I can attest that Jamison tackles its challenges head-on, telling the story that so many owners experience. He skillfully weaves together personal experiences and those of others to write a fable that is unmistakably 'true.'

I met Jamison many years ago at an IT event, and we quickly became friends. I had the fortune of walking with him as he grew his managed IT services provider (MSP) from a small company with few people to an organization of significant size and scale. It wasn't always a smooth ride, and we had numerous conversations along that bumpy road. In particular, the landscape of M&A involves emotions spanning the spectrum from joy to utter despair. And this aspect of business is far more profound than most people realize.

Emotion is always part of the M&A process on both sides of the table. But sellers bear a unique burden. It can be extremely impactful when the business you founded, built, and put decades of your life into is suddenly under new ownership.

Growing a business is similar to raising a family. Parents spend 18 years helping their kids mature into young adults, knowing that someday their children will take flight and move on to a life of their own. You do all you can to prepare them for success but often don't prepare yourself to let go. It's not much different when it comes to a business. Founders pour themselves into their company at startup, when they are the muscle behind everything. Then they spend years bringing on great teammates, developing lifelong customer relationships, and building something valuable that reflects who they are through the culture they created.

Then, poof: one day, it's gone.

Well, not quite that fast. But it sure feels that way. Moving from being a founder and owner to any other outcome is a major change, and very few are prepared for that reality.

I have the privilege of walking with many small business owners as they achieve this milestone. Unfortunately, and far too often after a sale, they describe being "lost," missing their purpose, and not having clear direction on what to do with the time, talent, and treasure they possess. In some cases, the word that describes them is "desolate." I've had more than one owner with a very successful exit tell me that the year after a sale was the most miserable of their life.

That's not how the world views selling a business successfully with a strong financial outcome. Usually, these transitions provide enough money for sellers to live the lifestyle they desire. But those feelings of despondency aren't about the money; they revolve around purpose and clarity about the future.

Being prepared is what sets one up for weathering both the sales process *and* achieving a great outcome. Outcomes vary broadly. But the one factor that seems to separate the good from the bad is the level of preparation and planning.

Another secret to success is doing all you can to take emotion out of the deal on both sides of the table. Having a list of non-negotiables created before you begin to entertain buyers frees you from needing to make emotional decisions while you negotiate. And having trusted advisors who can walk with you through the details and give honest feedback is also essential.

But understand that no matter what you do to prepare, emotion *will* have a seat at the table. And if it's not managed well, it can kill any deal at any time.

I hope you enjoy this fable that describes a very real story that plays out in countless small businesses. I've lived it personally and seen it happen dozens of times over the years.

If you are a business owner, the thing I wish for you more than anything else is to take action today and begin planning your exit. No one takes their business with them. You *will* have an exit or transition at some point. The sooner you embrace that fact and start preparing, the more likely a fantastic outcome will result.

Success is comprised of far more than money. Make time and prioritize starting the conversation around what your transition will look like. It can be wonderful. But a positive outcome will only happen if you plan it—and deliberately take action to make it so!

—ARLIN SORENSEN
VP ECOSYSTEM EVANGELISM AT CONNECTWISE

Preface

SELLING A BUSINESS USUALLY ISN'T EASY—and it's never simple. Even the smoothest deals based on the best exit planning are complex. And the small business owners with only an abstract idea of cashing out are in for some startling challenges that can be financial, moral, and, above all, emotional.

I've built, bought, and sold several businesses over the last 25 years while advising some colleagues and clients who sold or prepared to sell theirs. Every deal was different except for one thing: each had its own surprises.

I prepared for these challenges by reading everything I could get my hands on and learned many valuable lessons. But while plenty of books can teach you about valuations, contracts, and accounting, none of them prepare you for the *emotional* roller coaster of selling a business. *That* is why I wrote this book.

Small business owners go through a difficult journey after building something from the ground up and choosing to let it go. I've experienced this a few times and learned (and re-learned) that the black-and-white parts of a transaction pale in comparison to the emotional impact.

This book is written as a fictional fable that contains very non-fictional details. I chose this format after reading similar works, like

Michael Gerber's excellent *The E-Myth*, because it allows an author to convey thoughts, emotions, and motivations in a way that nonfiction cannot. A fable also allows me to combine my experiences with those of others to illustrate the surprises a seller may experience.

So, while the people and situations in this book are fictional, they are also *entirely realistic*.

Many realistic experiences have been altered, fused, and fit into an accessible story. The book also includes six case studies that are entirely true—and I am immensely grateful to everyone who agreed to tell their story.

I sincerely hope this book helps others not only prepare for a transaction but also avoid some common pitfalls. After a quarter-century in business, I value every experience—great and terrible—while cherishing all the good friends and fellow entrepreneurs who helped me tell this story.

—JAMISON WEST

The Grind

A LEX DREADED THIS MEETING and the conversation that would follow it even more. He checked his email one more time—another message from JJ, his biggest, most-demanding client. *I'll deal with him later.*

Alex sighed, stood up from his desk, and headed toward the conference room. It was five minutes to 10, and as the CEO and founder of A&S Digital Solutions, he was *never* late to the weekly leadership meeting.

This one would be a doozy. One of A&S's law firm clients had been hit with a ransomware attack a little over a week ago, and it had been all hands on deck to recover their data after running into problems with the backup. The previous leadership meeting had turned into a second ops meeting, and this one would probably be no different. There were some bigger issues Alex needed to discuss,

1

however. And given what the team had said the last time he brought up the subject, he steeled himself for frustration.

Alex entered the conference room and saw Kevin had beaten him to the table. A&S's sales manager was eager to please but arriving at meetings on time was about the only promise he kept. Alex would have preferred a salesperson who was late to meetings but hit his quarterly targets.

"Hey, Kevin. How are you?" he said.

"Great! Ready to hit the week and take down some big game!" came the inevitably chipper response.

Alex stifled a flash of irritation and nodded. Some days, he wondered if Kevin would try to sell him a used car. Hell, he might be better at it.

Acacia entered the room and dropped her stack of notebooks on the table, saving Alex from a few minutes of small talk. "Good morning, gentlemen." A&S's bookkeeper was quiet, competent, and reliable. Her invoices and payments were one of the few things in the managed IT services company that seemed to run on autopilot these days.

"How was your weekend?" said Kevin.

"Fine," came her typically restrained response. Soon, others filtered into the room.

Ron, the head of professional services, was a skilled technician but a prickly employee who sometimes pushed the limits of "telling it like it is." He'd probably be Alex's most significant challenge today. Dani, A&S's account manager, sat at the far end of the table. She tended to hesitate in leadership meetings that often turned technical and didn't contribute much, so she probably wouldn't raise objections. Now, they were just waiting on Mekhi, the managed services director, and Alex's right hand. Mekhi strode into the room five minutes late while staring at his phone.

"Sorry, guys," Mekhi said. "A meeting with the team ran late. We hit a new snag on JLC's data backup, but I think we've got it covered."

"Are we on track to get it all back?" Alex asked.

Mekhi looked up from his phone, paused, and gave a "probably" that didn't inspire complete confidence.

The meeting began, and it quickly became Mekhi's show. He detailed the latest efforts to handle the ransomware attack that had hit one of their law firm clients, explaining how they dealt with last week's snag and were tackling the new one. The team had discovered that several backups of client data failed, but the monitoring system was woefully inadequate and didn't report the problems ahead of time. The rest of the team was quiet as Mekhi, Ron, and Alex discussed the tech solutions and how to deploy the bulk of A&S's 21 employees to implement them. Alex looked at his phone and saw that 38 minutes had gone by.

"Hey guys, it sounds like we have a good handle on this. Let's take the rest offline or push it to the ops meeting," he said. "We've got some other stuff to go over."

Alex had their attention. *Ok, here goes.*

"So, this JLC situation is under control, but it could have gone bad. And being on the hook for losing a *law firm's* data wouldn't be something I'd want to deal with in court," he began. "Other clients, including JJ, don't follow nearly as many backup or security recommendations as JLC did. This is a problem. They're vulnerable, and so are we. I think it's time we bought Digital Shield and started using it."

Alex scanned the room. Mekhi pursed his lips. Kevin was nodding his head slightly while Ron audibly sighed. Only Acacia and Dani seemed unmoved, if attentive.

Alex had brought up Digital Shield for the first time three months ago and again a few weeks back, after he'd done more due diligence on the company and its product. Digital Shield was a Managed Security Services Provider (MSSP) that provided services directly to clients but also sold a full suite of cybersecurity tools to other IT companies. If A&S bought and implemented the platform, they'd vastly expand their ability to protect their clients from the growing threat of cyberattacks, plus open a new revenue stream—both of which Alex thought were sorely needed.

The team's first reaction to Digital Shield had been a "sounds interesting" that might have been a blow-off, probably because they never thought it would go any further. But Alex had met some resistance at the last mention—especially from Ron and, to a lesser extent, Mekhi. He didn't expect things would go better now that he was seriously proposing it.

"We're not a cybersecurity firm," Ron said.

Here we go, thought Alex.

"And we barely have the resources to keep up with what we're doing today," Ron continued. "How are we supposed to learn the platform and become security experts when we can barely keep our heads above water doing the projects and clients we have? I think it's a bad idea. Farm it out to them and white-label their services, maybe."

Alex glanced at Mekhi but didn't catch a reaction.

"I'd be able to sell that," offered Kevin. "Ransomware is a big threat, and fear can drive sales."

"Thanks, Kevin. Ron: I understand there would be a learning curve, and we'd have to find the time to implement it," Alex said. "But the fact is that ransomware isn't going away; it's becoming a bigger and bigger threat to our clients and us. Half of our accounts aren't sufficiently protected as it is, and you've spent most of the last two weeks working on a problem that isn't even your department's job. In the end, fewer breaches could *save* time."

"Then, there is the risk of not getting into this. Say that JLC didn't have the infrastructure they did and lost everything," Alex continued. "We'd be on the hook for making it right. As their MSP, certainly technologically. Maybe financially and legally. And one big fight like that could put us out of business. Now, think of the clients who've refused to follow our recommendations, like Randall dodging us on setting up multi-factor authentication. They're vulnerable. And as a result, so are we."

"It's just not practical," Ron rebutted. "If you want better security, just partner with them and let them handle—"

"Hold on a sec; let me finish," said Alex, putting his hand up. "Then, there are our numbers. We've had a pretty good few years after a nasty one, but sales have slowed down." Alex avoided looking at Kevin.

"Our competition has grown, and everybody is offering pretty much the same thing," he added. "A full suite of cybersecurity services will set us apart, at least for now. It will also let us upsell current clients and add a new revenue stream. We can't take this company to the next level on referrals alone. I've considered white labeling their services, but we'd make very little, if any money in that arrangement. And they provide some of the things we already do. If we expose our clients to them, they might drive a wedge between us and wind up taking a few with them if the partnership doesn't work. Ok, go ahead."

"I get it," allowed Ron. "But we don't have the expertise or the time. There's a benefit to doing a few things really well rather than doing everything half-assed. If we want to hire five more people with cybersecurity expertise, go for it." He folded his arms and went silent.

Alex shifted his attention to Mekhi, who seemed lost in thought. The managed services director cleared his throat and started cleaning his glasses, a tell-tale sign he was about to speak.

"I see the benefit of getting deeper into cybersecurity," he said. "And I've briefly looked over Digital Shield's tools. They seem to have a good set of off-the-shelf products and proprietary features in their platform and seem to know what they're doing." Alex dared to hope.

"But Ron has a point," Mekhi continued. "I'm saying they 'seem to' because I don't really *know* if they are good. And I don't know that because I don't have enough time to conduct due diligence, much less learn how to use those tools. I don't even have time to get us on top of our current clients. Buying this, learning the platform, and servicing clients on a new thing? Adding all that to the mix doesn't seem realistic right now. But I do see the value in eventually doing this."

Et tu, Brute? thought Alex. *No, that's not fair.*

Mekhi usually had his back, and Alex knew that the objections he and Ron were raising were valid. The company always seemed like it was operating at max capacity handling the current load while onboarding one or two clients a quarter. But he also knew that if A&S were to survive *and* grow, something had to change. Sure, they were keeping the ship sailing. In fact, the company was doing well. But Alex couldn't shake the feeling they were headed for a cybersecurity iceberg.

He asked Acacia and Dani for their perspectives since the rest of the team had dominated the meeting. Dani showed cautious but vague optimism, while Acacia matter-of-factly said that "accounting won't be a problem." *Oh, to get that reaction from everyone else,* Alex thought. *Nobody wants to help with strategic decisions, but I can just point her at something, and she handles it.*

"Ok. Well, we're two minutes to 11," Alex said. "Let's table this for next week; I'll bring some numbers. And I'd like a few minutes with you, Mekhi."

The meeting broke up, and Mekhi walked with Alex to his office. They briefly discussed the JLM data recovery and how Mekhi's new level-one tech was doing before moving on to Digital Shield.

"Look, I get it. And I'm sorry if it seems like I'm undercutting you," Mekhi said. "I just don't know … *operationally*, how we can handle onboarding it without letting something else slide."

Mekhi listed numerous barriers while again admitting that an expansion into cybersecurity was, strategically, a good idea. Alex was frustrated by the lack of enthusiasm, but he couldn't be angry at his 32-year-old managed services director, who was really more like a vice president.

Mekhi was exceptionally good at his job, worked incredibly hard, and the company couldn't run without him. He *was* buried in operations, which didn't get any easier fighting fires like ransomware attacks. But Alex also knew that they couldn't strike a partnership with Digital Shield without Mekhi's buy-in and help. He just wished, for a second, that Mekhi would approach the problem with "here's how we get this done" instead of "here's why we can't do this." Alex asked when they might have the bandwidth for implementation.

"I'm not sure. Maybe Q3," Mekhi said. "We'd probably need to expand the team *or* work with what we have and drop some projects or clients."

Alex thanked Mekhi for his input and asked him to close the door on his way out. As he'd anticipated, Alex was frustrated.

Dropping any business that would make a time difference was a non-starter, and hiring new people might not be feasible. A&S and its margins were doing ok, though another huge problem or two like the ransomware attack could throw profit out the window. And Digital Shield cost a decent sum, along with the man-hours it would take to expand the services. Alex could squirrel away some money, get a loan, or, God forbid, not take his very reasonable salary again. He could also just outsource Managed Security Services to another company. But one way or another, it would be a risk. And though he would never admit it to his team, he also felt a little uncomfortable with the new technology.

Alex had founded A&S 18 years ago—the S was for Steve, his former partner—when managed IT services didn't really exist. It was all "time and materials" back then, and he'd started out as a one-man enterprise by fixing some server problems for an accounting firm, followed by another contract setting up software for one of their clients. One job led to another, and Steve had come on board to make it a real company. A&S slowly but surely grew, hiring their first employee 16 years ago, and eventually switched over to managed services mixed with a steady handful of pay-for-play projects.

Those early years had been hard—Alex both winced and felt proud when he thought of the long hours and stress. They'd successfully built a stable company before Steve left for a great opportunity developing software. The two had parted amicably, and he missed working with his old partner. Alex missed the friendship, sure. But what he really could have used was Steve's tech skills and perspective. It was lonely as the sole founder and CEO, and especially isolating being the only person who seemed to think or even care about strategy.

The IT landscape was evolving, and ransomware wasn't the only thing that kept Alex awake at night. Back in the day, he'd spent most of his time installing servers or helping someone get their email up and running. Now, the technology was changing at an accelerated pace. The move to cloud architecture and the security demands that came along with it. The shift to software as a service. The remote work trend and all the headaches of trying to troubleshoot diverse networks and devices.

Alex and A&S adapted with the changes. But at heart, he was an old tech who loved turning screwdrivers on servers. At 48 years old, he wondered what was next and whether he would have the energy to keep up.

Then, there was the industry. Managed IT services had become a commodity, and there seemed to be a ceiling on getting new business.

Alex could blame Kevin for not hitting his sales numbers—or the three sales managers who'd preceded him—but the truth was that A&S had always had a problem with marketing and sales. The competition had grown around Philadelphia like everywhere else in the country, and everyone essentially offered the same services. The only things that set a company apart were the level and speed of service it provided and the referrals that created. Managed IT seemed as much like a popularity contest as a technological showcase these days—success depended on who liked you more.

A&S *was* stable and profitable, however. After losing some key clients a few years ago and working 12-hour days to right the ship, the company had experienced three consecutive profitable years. He actually got to spend time with his wife and kids again and had gained a lot of confidence in his team. But good ROI always seemed like a near-run thing in managed services—they were always one tech crisis away from losing it—and parts of his team were still overworked. The company had to grow its revenue to expand the team safely, but it also had to evolve to grow. And that probably meant becoming a premier cybersecurity provider or developing some killer piece of intellectual property. Alex wasn't sure he had the energy, time, cash, or enthusiastic support to make any of that happen.

The phone rang, and he looked at the caller ID. *JJ. Better deal with this now.*

"Hey, JJ—how's it going?"

"Hi, Alex—not bad. But we have a problem with the remote access to our ERP platform again, and it doesn't seem like your guys are figuring it out. Can you take a look?"

Alex listened patiently and asked a few questions before getting off the phone with a promise to take care of the issue. He knew the support ticket was undoubtedly in the queue, and Mekhi's team was probably already on it. Nevertheless, JJ liked to go above everyone's head to accelerate things. And as A&S's biggest client responsible for about 20% of the company's revenue, he knew that he could get special attention from Alex whenever he wanted it.

That was another problem and vulnerability, Alex knew. The day JJ stopped calling and took his business elsewhere was a day when A&S lost a fifth of its business. The relationship wasn't particularly profitable, and it was a genuine pain to drop everything and service one client. But that cash covered the salary of a lot of employees. Alex lost a lot of sleep wondering what they'd do if JJ walked.

He messaged Mekhi and asked him about the support ticket. Sure enough, it was in the queue and being worked on. He told Mekhi to email JJ to let him know the status.

Ok, time to get some actual work done.

Alex had a lunch meeting with a prospective client and wanted to play around with spreadsheets to see what he could do to make Digital Shield happen. Another email came in. It was from Frank, who owned a managed IT services firm outside Princeton.

The subject line was "Let's catch up!"

Alex was pretty sure he knew what that meant. Frank had first propositioned him about selling A&S four years ago and again two years after that. This might be his latest fishing expedition. One tried-and-true way to bust through the managed IT services growth ceiling was to buy another firm and take on its clients. Frank wanted Alex's clients and geographic footprint. Alex started typing a reply but paused.

I wonder what he'd offer. A good number of clients, $2 million in revenue … that's gotta be a multiple of …

Alex finished his reply and hit send. They'd probably see each other at the big vendor conference in a month, but Alex told Frank to go ahead and drop a meeting in his calendar whenever he was available.

Might as well see what he has to say.

Curiosity

ALEX PULLED INTO THE RESTAURANT'S parking about 20 minutes late. He'd been caught up in another meeting on the JLM data recovery, and the traffic hadn't been ideal. The upscale steakhouse wasn't exactly close to the office, though it was nearer to his than Frank's. This accommodation, along with the nice venue—Frank had gained a reputation for being a cheapskate at networking dinners—further clued him in to the lunch's agenda.

Alex texted his arrival, and Frank replied that he was in a booth in the back. Alex soon found his paunchy, middle-aged industry colleague and indirect competitor, an untouched water and a half-empty scotch on the table in front of him. *Good old Frank. Starting early.* He also had a reputation for hitting up the cocktails at industry events.

"Sorry I'm late, Frank. Got pulled into fighting a fire and hit some traffic," Alex said as he shook hands and sat down.

"No problem, buddy. I caught up on some emails," came the reply. "How's business?"

Straight to the point. Alex wasn't sure if Frank even knew if he was married or had kids, given their typical conversations.

"We're doing good," Alex replied. "Busy. We're in the middle of a big project, so it's a little hectic right now. But not too bad. How are things at your shop?"

"Great," said Frank. "What's this project?"

"Well, it's a data recovery." Alex paused; there was no sense advertising any weakness if Frank was going to pitch a buy. "A client was hit with a bug, but we got them up and running quickly."

Frank laughed. "Unavoidable, these days. And usually a royal pain in the ass. Glad you are on top of it."

The two men ordered food and briefly discussed Frank's fishing trip to the Florida Keys, the upcoming conference, and a new CRM platform rollout. Then Frank looked at Alex squarely.

"So—have you considered selling the company lately?" said Frank. "Because we might be seriously interested in buying it."

"Not really. I haven't given it much thought," Alex answered truthfully. "We just had our best year ever. But never say never, I guess. It would depend on the offer."

"Well, if you guys are doing as well as you say, it would be a good one," said Frank. "About how many customers do you have these days?"

"We might be onboarding a couple soon, so it's about 60 or so."

Alex knew that it was the clients and geographic footprint he was after. Frank ran a slightly bigger MSP located about an hour away. And while South Brunswick, NJ was close to Princeton and

Trenton and had a good customer base and market, A&S would get him nearer to Philadelphia.

"What's your revenue look like?" Frank asked.

"A bit over $2 million."

"Hmmm. Well, you know, we'd pay a fair price and multiple for our industry, assuming the due diligence all worked out—ISPs can range from three to five times net," Frank said.

"Not bad," Alex responded as he furiously solved the math problem. *$2 million in revenue, $400k profit, a multiplier of five ... 2 million dollars. Not bad at all.*

Alex wasn't playing hard to get by telling Frank he hadn't considered selling. He'd been so buried in getting A&S on track that it probably hadn't crossed his mind in years. But $2 million in his pocket was a number that got his attention—and that was right out of the gate. Alex thought some businesses sold for higher multiples, and the actual number probably depended on how badly Frank wanted the company and clients. *He's asked me about selling three times over the years—could I get more?*

"Well, I'll consider it," Alex said. "What would be your plan after buying it?"

Predictably, Frank said he was interested in expanding and broadening his firm's footprint. He also said he wasn't "interested in fixing what ain't broke," and if A&S was running as well as it seemed, he could smoothly integrate the two companies' services. They discussed a few more general numbers in between mouthfuls of food before talking about processes and platforms, and it seemed like the two MSPs had a lot in common. Alex looked at his phone.

"Well, I have to get back. This has been interesting," he said. "Like I said, I haven't considered selling. But let me give it some thought."

"You do that!" said Frank with a laugh and a smile. "No, no, put your wallet away. I've got the check."

The two men shook hands and headed to their cars. Alex opened the door of his sedan and sat down but paused after putting the key in the ignition.

"Huh!" he said to the steering wheel. "Maybe two million dollars. What could I do with *that*?"

Lost in thought, he started driving back to the office. Maybe—just maybe—a solution to his worries about the business had been staring him in the face. He'd had an 18-year run. And 48 years old might be slightly young to retire but not old enough that he couldn't do something else—whatever he wanted, really. But sell A&S? It was his baby and, in many ways, his life. Running the firm had consumed him for so long that it was hard to imagine what might come next.

After the early years of struggle and painful growth, the company had crested the $1 million revenue mark and broke through the tough ceiling of 10 employees. A&S had found stability a little over a decade ago, or what passed for it in managed IT services. The hours were still long and the minor management problems seemingly endless, but the firm had been running pretty smoothly. Then, four years ago, disaster hit.

The economy had taken a dip, and five clients, including one responsible for 10% of revenue, had either folded or downsized, yanking their MSP services or downgrading them. Compounding the hit was turnover—three extremely valuable techs had left in quick succession for better opportunities. Seemingly overnight, A&S had been in trouble.

Alex had worked his network to find new clients while auditing and adapting both processes and the pay and benefits structure. The effort had worked. A&S gained efficiencies along with a compensation plan that kept and attracted the employees he needed. But the net result was paying more with less revenue as onboarding new clients lagged the necessary changes. There had been quarters when making payroll was a near-run thing, even with Alex not taking his salary.

The existential phase of the struggle had lasted about a year and a half—18 months of constant stress, 12-hour days, and essentially ignoring his family. Alex had missed baseball games, relaxing weekends, and even forgot his wife's birthday, all while wondering whether A&S would ever pull out of the nosedive. The pressure was intense, and his diet and health had suffered—Alex gained 20 pounds he'd never entirely shed, mostly from eating take-out at his desk and hitting a little whiskey when he got home. Looking back, it was the worst period in his life. Constant worry about failure while being responsible for his family's financial security and the welfare of his employees had taken a big toll.

Thankfully, all the sacrifice—and a bit of luck—had paid off. A new profit-sharing plan had found and kept crucial employees. And A&S had signed some new clients, including JJ, whose revenue covered a lot of overhead. The firm had emerged from the struggle stronger than before, with new processes and offerings. The previous three years had seen slow but steady growth, with last quarter being the best the company had ever seen in revenue.

Nevertheless, sales seemed harder to come by, and the suddenness of the previous disaster had scarred Alex. Before it hit, things had also seemed to be doing well. He'd never quite feel secure again as he wondered what might be just around the corner.

Would the economy crash? Could they cope with the exploding rate of cybercrime? What if Mekhi left the company? How much market in this area was left?

And the most persistent worry: *Do I have the energy to deal with the changes in this industry—or another crisis?*

Balancing that anxiety was pride in turning things around and reading financial statements with satisfaction instead of fear. A&S was profitable, pulling in about $400k a year. Five more years of merely treading water, and he might rake in nearly a couple of million dollars. But a lot could happen in five years. If he sold now, he might get that sum—or more—without the stress of dealing with the unknown.

Alex snapped to attention when he spotted his firm's parking lot. It was like the car had been on autopilot for the 20-minute drive. His phone had buzzed with ignored texts that he now checked. There was another ad hoc meeting request, and JJ asking for an update on his project's status.

Stop daydreaming and get back in the game.

‹'֍֎#

Kristi heard the garage door open and finished setting the table. The boys were staying over at a friend's house, so it was a paper plate and Chinese food night. Alex had sent her a vaguely mysterious text asking if she would be home by 6:30 and mentioning something he wanted to discuss. The question was odd because she always beat him home on Wednesdays. Kristi taught economics at a local college, and he knew her last class ended at four.

Alex opened the door, threw his keys and several bags of food on the counter, and gave her a hug and a kiss.

"Hey hon, how was your day?" she asked. "What's the big talk?"

Alex smiled as he kicked his shoes off and poured two glasses of wine.

"Well, not that big a deal," he said. "Remember Frank, who runs the MSP over in Jersey? He asked if I wanted to sell A&S again. Only this time, I'm … well, I'm actually kinda thinkin' about it. What do you think?"

The record in Kristi's head skipped. That *would* be something big.

"No idea," she laughed. "Though, pretty sure we could live ok on a couple of hundred million dollars. What's the offer? Any details?"

"Not really; just some general interest and maybe a ballpark figure. I doubt a couple of hundo is on the table," Alex said with a smile. "Near as I can figure, the offer *might* wind up around two. Maybe more if our financials are strong enough and he wants my clients bad enough."

"Huh. Well, we could certainly make *that* work," she said. "But this is kind of out of the blue. When did you start thinking about selling? And what would you want to do if you did?"

The last question was the crucial one. Kristi had been with Alex and the business through thick and thin, lean years and windfalls. She had witnessed her husband pour every ounce of his being into that company and even done so herself, years ago. Kristi served as

A&S's official bookkeeper and unofficial operations manager in the early years, briefly putting her career on hold to help stabilize the company. She'd eventually left when things settled down and A&S had enough revenue to hire outside help—and their marriage had been the better for it.

Even so, a little distance hadn't inoculated her or the kids from the challenges of running the business. She'd counseled Alex, helped him with the struggle, and watched him start to crack under immense pressure four years ago. This stress had bled into their marriage and caused minor fights, mostly about his absence from their boys' lives for the better part of a year. Thankfully, the family had gotten Alex "back" from A&S a couple of years ago. The company's specter still loomed large, however.

So, in one significant respect, she was thrilled by the idea of him selling the business. But that excitement was tempered by surprise—and a little worry about what he'd do afterward.

A&S is such a huge part of his life—who he is. Hell, it's part of what this family is. What comes after that? she thought.

"Honestly, I hadn't thought about selling," Alex said. "Frank just contacted me. He probably has a calendar reminder to do it every other year. But this time, it kind of resonated. As for what I'd do, no idea! But taking a break for a while sounds pretty nice, you know?"

"Yeah. So, why are you considering it now?" Kristi said. "And don't take that as resistance or anything. I'm perfectly fine with the idea—as long as you get a deal that makes sense. Just curious why it got your attention now. The company's doing well, isn't it?"

Alex confirmed the financials were good but noted that they'd have to stay that way for several years to make an income equivalent to a good sale. Then he vented about his worries: the changing MSP landscape, cybercrime, the economy, and, after some prodding, whether he would have the energy to tackle the next big challenge, whatever it was.

"I'd always assumed that after you hit a certain level of success—like, $2 million in revenue—the business would mostly run without me," he said. "And ops do, to a big extent. But I'm still handling most of the sales. And I'm the only one thinking strategically and looking for ways to execute on whatever plan. Truth be told, Kristi, it's a little lonely. If we could walk away with a nice chunk of change, I could do something else. Hell, our family could do something else. We don't even need to stay here if you want to teach somewhere else. We could kiss Philly winters goodbye."

Kristi wasn't sure about pulling up roots and leaving her job, though her parents lived in Florida, and she could find another position. *Maybe.* But the more she thought about it, selling might make sense. They weren't getting any younger, and Alex's anxiety about the future worried her a little. They'd put away a decent sum of money, and the kids' college funds were on track. If the family could achieve financial security in one fell swoop instead of sweating out five more years ... well, that might add a few years to Alex's life in the long run. And he'd find something else to do. Hopefully, it would be something a little less stressful.

"One thing at a time, dear. But ... I'm on board if a deal makes sense," she said. "Where does the offer go from here?"

"Good question," Alex said. "I haven't really prepped an exit plan or run any numbers. And who knows if Frank is even the best deal I could get. I need to do some research and reach out to some friends.

You know, get some advice from some folks who know what the hell they are doing. This is all preliminary, and I might be putting the cart before the horse. Let's figure out what the company is really worth and see what the market interest might be."

"Sounds like a plan. We gonna eat?" Kristi said.

The bags of Chinese food sat unopened and undoubtedly cold. Alex laughed, grabbed the food, and headed for the microwave.

Euphoria

ALEX PULLED INTO THE A&S parking lot at 7 a.m., which should give him at least an hour until anyone else arrived. He unlocked the front door and made a beeline for the coffee machine before heading to his office.

Alex hit the light, closed the door, and fired up his computer. He switched the wireless connection from the company Wi-Fi to his smartphone's hotspot, opened up a private browser, and started typing.

"business valuation"

Even though he was alone with his thoughts and a search engine, Alex was vaguely embarrassed. He'd enthusiastically thrown himself into entrepreneurship years ago, reading many classic business primers and strategy books. And his CPA asked him about his exit strategy every so often, chiding him to plan for the future. But Alex simply hadn't given exit planning the attention it deserved, at least according to every business guru worth their salt. He couldn't even remember all of the different valuation methods.

Alex clicked on a link for "business valuation:"

Asset-based, discounted cash flow, revenue/earnings, and market value methods. The first one won't apply; the third is what I'd assumed. Market value is interesting; where do I get comps of other local MSPs that have sold recently?

"business value calculator"

This search yielded confusing results. Different calculators had different fields, some of which Alex couldn't fill in with confidence. He wasn't sure what A&S's realistic projected annual growth rate should be or how long it would last, and he had to look up "excess compensation" to confirm the meaning. *Nothing really seems 'excess' about my pay.*

Some of the calculators' results were pleasing, depending on the variables. But others seemed a little low—less than the five-times-profit multiple that served as his baseline.

"how to sell a business"

"Prepare your strategy in advance." *Well, that ship has sailed.* "Get an independent valuation." *Definitely.* "Hire a broker." *Hmm.*

Alex switched over to his email. He routinely received messages from merger and acquisition (M&A) firms asking if he was interested in selling. After weeding out the pitches that seemed unprofessional, Alex had a list. He made a mental note to ask some colleagues in his local networking group for references, though he'd have to be careful about letting everyone know he was interested in selling.

After about an hour of research, Alex also had a list of information he needed to get a better idea of A&S's value, along with some other questions that needed answers. One item, in particular, bothered him: "Clean up the financials."

Like most business owners, Alex had mixed some of his personal and business finances to reap tax advantages, and he wondered whether that would be a problem. But the biggest takeaway on how to increase A&S's value was to either bring in more revenue or lower expenses. Selling to more clients was possible but unlikely in a short timeframe. And a buyer would probably see through quickly cutting costs when they looked at the books, not to mention employees asking questions. Alex did gain one valuable piece of information and course of action, however: there was no sense in taking on *new* expenses if he was thinking of selling anytime soon.

Looks like Digital Shield isn't a good idea right now. Still, the valuation numbers are looking pretty good, even without any hocus-pocus.

Some of the results from valuation calculators had seemed a little low, to the extent Alex could confidently fill in the fields. But one industry website reported that MSPs with profit margins up to 7.5% often sold for *6.2 times* their Earnings Before Interest, Taxes, Depreciation, and Amortization (EBITDA), not the multiple of five that Frank had mentioned. That would put the sale price as high as almost $2.5 million! [1]

There was a knock at the door, and Alex reflexively hit the keys to minimize all applications.

"Come in," he said, realizing that he'd totally lost track of time.

---

[1] Panettieri, Joe. "MSP Mergers, Acquisitions, Valuations: Essential CEO and CFO Planning Tips." CHANNELe2e. https://www.channele2e.com/investors/mergers-acquisitions/msp-mergers-acquisitions-valuations-essential-ceo-and-cfo-planning-tips/

"Hey, boss. You're in here early," Mekhi said as he walked into the room. "Got a minute?"

"Sure."

Mekhi sat down and briefed Alex on the status of JLM: the team had completed the data recovery and upgraded the backups. The client wasn't precisely happy they'd been hacked, but they did seem pleased with A&S's response. Further, the law firm was spooked enough to agree to all the proactive security measures that Mekhi and his team recommended.

"They won't be immune to another attack, but it should plug some holes," Mekhi said. "And I recommend we bring in a security firm to do a complete audit to make sure the hackers didn't leave anything nasty behind."

"Ok, thanks. Let me give that some thought," Alex responded.

Mekhi got up to leave but paused at the door.

"Look, Alex: I'm sorry if I haven't been supportive about Digital Shield," he said. "It's not a bad idea; I'm just not sure if we can do it at the moment. But now that this fire is put out, let me sit down and try to think of how that might work."

Alex raised an eyebrow a little as he looked at Mekhi. He was a little taken aback at the offer for proactive help but more surprised at the display of sincerity. A&S's managed services director was competent, efficient, and reliable. Emotion and vulnerability weren't usually in his wheelhouse, however.

Mekhi had started out as a level-one tech when Alex hired him eight years ago. Within a year, he managed a team, and he'd been promoted to director within two. Mekhi was insanely knowledgeable about the job's technical aspects and even more skilled at managing the processes that got things done. He viewed every ticket, project, and task as an engineering problem to be solved with meticulously mapped out "orders of operations." Then he tackled an issue relentlessly but, crucially, with enough flexibility.

Mekhi wasn't exactly a people person. But he was fair, and the techs respected him and his approach enough to qualify him as a good leader. For Alex and A&S, he was a godsend. Mekhi was one of the essential elements that had enabled the company to bust through the one-million-dollar mark. Alex could put much of operations in a mental box marked "taken care of" and focus on the other aspects of running a business. He sometimes forgot that and took his managed services director for granted, but he was reminded of it now.

"Hey man, no problem. And I really appreciate that," Alex said with sincerity. "Don't worry too much about Digital Shield and make sure you prioritize the immediate stuff on your plate. I'm looking into it, and we'll figure something out. But thank you. Hey, do you know if Acacia is in?"

Mekhi grunted and nodded. "Of course. It's 8:30. She's probably been here for an hour already." He did one of his signature awkward waves and headed toward his desk.

Alex walked over to Acacia's office.

"Good morning," Alex said as he rapped his knuckles on the doorframe.

"Good morning," came the even response.

"When you have a moment, I need some numbers," he said. Alex requested the last five years of detailed P&Ls, expense summaries, and any projections she'd whipped up, among a few other items. "Any chance I could get those today?"

"Yes. Of course," Acacia said. Then she looked at him squarely, though without apparent emotion. "Why do you need them?"

Alex consciously remained nonchalant. He'd expected the question and mentally rehearsed a generic answer. But there was something about Acacia that always seemed omniscient. It was like her impassive eyes saw right through him.

"Just running some numbers and trying to plan. Maybe for Digital Shield." He grimaced inwardly at the extra lie, which was probably unnecessary.

"Roger that," Acacia said as she turned back to her screen. "I'll have them for you by 11."

"Thanks."

∿'📣⚑ #

Alex set up shop on a corner table at a local restaurant, just after the lunch crowd had left. There was no way he was going to make these calls in the office.

First on the list was Frank. Alex called him and expressed interest in discussing a possible sale, and Frank's response was enthusiastic. Alex had meant to merely set up another meeting, but Frank peppered him with questions about the business, including its exact revenue, some key clients, and Alex's take-home pay. Frank seemed satisfied with the answers and once again suggested a possible 5x multiplier, "assuming all the numbers work out." Alex held back on mentioning the higher, industry-specific multiplier he'd uncovered. *We'll get into that later. Maybe when I have another possible buyer.*

Next up was a broker. Alex had put out some feelers to his network asking for recommendations of business brokers or merger and acquisition firms and let a select few individuals know he was interested in selling. One firm—the Johnston Group—had received high marks from a friend. Alex dialed them up, said he was interested in selling his business, and waited as he was transferred to a "lead broker agent."

"Hello, Alex. This is Mike. I'm a lead agent here at Johnston, and I hear you're looking to sell your MSP. Tell me a little bit about the company and why you're selling."

Alex recited many of the details he'd shared with Frank, plus a few more items that he'd read were key to valuation. As for why he was selling, he mentioned that he'd received a preliminary offer and "just decided it might be time to sell."

"Are there any critical employees that will need to come along as part of the deal?" asked Mike.

Alex hadn't thought of that. Mekhi, definitely. Certainly not Kevin, and maybe Ron. Dani was pretty valuable. So was Acacia, but companies tended to have their own bookkeepers or accountants.

"One or two, maybe. I'm not sure. Probably depends on the buyer," said Alex. "Given what I've told you, what would the price look like? I've seen five times profit thrown around, but some MSPs seem to sell for six or even more. What do you think I could get?"

"Well, it's early and a little hard to put an exact number on things without all the due diligence," Mike said. "But you are definitely in the ballpark. If A&S is running well, we can probably easily get you five. Maybe more."

Alex smiled as he waved the waiter away. *$2 million at least. Maybe $2.4. Hell, maybe there will be a bidding war, and it will be even higher!*

"Sounds good. What else—"

"But before we go into any more specifics," Mike interrupted, "we're going to need to sign a non-disclosure agreement. An NDA will allow us to get into the details while protecting everyone. When we have a buyer, we'll do a separate NDA with them, of course."

Slightly chastened, Alex wondered if he'd overshared a little—with the broker *and* Frank.

"I'll have that emailed over to you right after this call," continued Mike. "If you want to move forward with us, sign and send it back to me. And let's set up an hour-long sit-down for later this week."

The two men checked their schedules and settled on meeting in Johnston's offices on Thursday at three.

"I'm really excited to have the chance to work with you," Mike said as they ended the call. "MSPs do tend to have a higher multiple than average, and a lot of buyers are interested in this sector. I'm sure we can get you a number that you'll be very happy with."

Alex thanked him and hung up. He closed his laptop, put it in his bag, and called the waiter over.

"Ready to order? And would you like more water, sir?"

"Yes. I'll have the surf and turf special. Medium rare," Alex said. "And … what's your best scotch?"

"We've got a Glenlivet 18 and Johnnie Walker Blue."

"Johnnie Walker. One ice cube, please."

Alex picked up his phone again and texted his wife: "numbers are looking good!!!! ☺"

꙾⥈☙⥌#

"What do you think, Alex?"

Alex started slightly at the mention of his name. Ron and Mekhi were discussing a customer's request and trying to decide whether it fell under the service-level agreement or constituted a special project. Alex had zoned out for at least two-thirds of the conversation during the weekly leadership meeting.

"I'm not sure. How much new hardware is needed?" he covered. Ron explained the requirements and, from his tone, it was something they'd just discussed.

"Ok. Let's take this offline. Please itemize that and the overall request in an email. I want to give it some thought," Alex said. "Kevin: why don't you catch us up on sales?"

Kevin launched into his weekly recitation of sales contacts and promising prospects, but Alex soon tuned out again. He bounced between thinking about the steps needed to complete a sale of A&S and daydreaming about the aftermath. In the past week, Alex had more meetings with the broker and Frank—one NDA was signed, and the other was imminent. Alex had also contacted his accountant and lawyer to let them know that he was exploring a sale. The attorney had green-lit the broker's NDA and would soon evaluate Frank's.

If Alex were completely honest with himself, he'd have to admit that "exploring a sale" was a lie. Yes, he might be cautiously evaluating Frank's deal, the M&A firm, and whatever prospective buyers the latter would bring to the table. But he was almost definitely selling. Alex had gone from curiosity to barely contained elation in the past week. The possible numbers looked good—really good—and when he thought of what he could do with all that money …

It would buy freedom—financial, professional, and psychological liberty.

We've already taken care of the kids' college funds, and we have a decent nest egg socked away. With an extra two or two and a half mill, we could do whatever we want.

Kristi had been supportive, and Alex had even detected a little excitement creeping into her logical advice. She demurred when he mentioned moving, but the suggestion that she take summer semesters off and they travel around the world had gotten her attention. Then, there was the question of what he'd do with himself.

Start another business? Get more involved with the peer group? Learn to play golf?

Alex silently chuckled at the last idea. He couldn't picture himself running around golf courses and drinking Long Island iced teas for the rest of his time on the planet. Alex had always played around with coding, though it had been a few years. Maybe he'd develop a killer app, learn some new (human) languages, or even write a book. In truth, the details didn't matter. He'd find something to do, and it wouldn't be this.

Running a business had its high points and could be incredibly satisfying. But the thing that most captivated Alex about selling was the idea of being free. Free from the total responsibility and accountability. Liberated from the stress, anxiety, and problems, mundane and existential, he alone was ultimately responsible for solving. Alex loved his business, and he was immensely proud of it. But it was almost as if the dollar signs had flipped a switch in his head. He'd toiled, sweated, and stressed for years, and now the thing he'd built was valuable. If Alex had the opportunity to cash in and learn to enjoy life a little more—whatever form that took—why not? Eighteen years of running the company were enough.

A couple of million dollars. A fresh start. A world of possibilities. Holy shit.

Alex pulled out of the reverie as Kevin completed his update. He wrapped up the meeting with a promise to give Mekhi and Ron a ruling on the client's upgrade request. Mekhi tapped him on the shoulder in the hallway.

"Hey man, you alright? You seem a little out of it," Mekhi said.

"Oh, sorry, yeah. I just didn't get a great night's sleep. But otherwise, I'm good. Fantastic, even," he said with a smile.

Posturing
and Caution

May 12th

ALEX REREAD THE EMAIL. A couple of things were a surprise, though he knew they shouldn't be; the requests were logical and fair. Alex had just been so focused on the idea of a sale that he'd glossed over the details of getting ready for one. Now, he wasn't sure how to fulfill one ask. And broaching the subject with someone who had the answers might set off alarm bells in his business.

Alex had signed a non-disclosure agreement with Frank almost two weeks ago, and that NDA was followed by a second one a week later. The M&A broker had brought him another interested buyer: a local managed services provider that was a direct competitor. While Alex knew who the owner was, he didn't know him well. They'd only met briefly at a networking event.

There were now three NDAs: one with Frank, one with the new prospect, and one with the business brokerage. These documents allowed each party to have more transparent conversations, and Alex had done three calls so far and answered a few emails. Frank and Alex spoke directly in two talks, while the other prospective buyer's questions were filtered through the broker. Both interested parties were asking some questions about Alex's business for which he didn't have easy answers.

That first post-NDA call with Frank went well, though it opened Alex's eyes a little.

Frank asked him who his key employees were, how long they'd been with the firm, what they were paid, and whether they were content working there. None of those items was a problem. Alex spoke enthusiastically about Mekhi and his skill, boasting that he was the "best IT manager in the business." He also mentioned Ron's value as a project manager while glossing over whether Ron liked working at the firm. In truth, that guy *never* seemed happy. Alex ballparked both of their salaries without getting into the potential bonuses.

Frank also requested A&S's high-level profit and loss numbers going back three years and dug into the client list a bit, asking about the biggest customers and how much revenue they provided. Alex told him about JJ and that he represented a fifth of the business's revenue—without revealing what a pain in the ass JJ could be.

"Hmmm. Are they on contract? What are the terms?" was Frank's response.

"The contract is a yearly agreement, though there is a termination clause with a 30-day waiting period if they think the terms of the SLA aren't being met," answered Alex.

"Hmmm."

Frank had moved on, leaving Alex a little worried. *Is a client as big as JJ a risk that will lower the offer price?*

A few of the questions had this effect. There wasn't anything aggressive about the conversations, but Frank's commonsense asks probed for chinks in A&S's armor that Alex hadn't considered. And they seemed to find some.

There were some positive aspects, however. When their conversation steered toward systems, tech, and processes, Frank and Alex discovered that their firms had many similarities. And Frank's line of questioning backed up his stated intent: he aimed to buy Alex's business and keep it mostly intact. Frank wanted something resembling a new branch of his existing firm, not to 'strip A&S for parts' by only snapping up clients and a few employees.

In contrast, the other possible buyer didn't seem as interested in purchasing A&S whole or at least keeping it that way. All the questions so far—asked through the broker—centered on revenue, profits, clients, and contracts, emphasizing the last two. They'd asked about key employees but didn't dive into how the MSP worked. Perhaps Alex was misreading things, but he was starting to get the sense that prospective buyer might fire a lot of people.

Frank was pulling ahead as an attractive deal, but his email today presented a new challenge:

1. Can you give me a high-level summary of the number of clients by contract type?
2. For example, are they all one-year with a 30-day SLA escape clause?
Happy to jump on a call!

Alex knew the answer to the second question: "no." He couldn't complete the first ask without some research, however. A&S had standardized *most* of its contracts to one-year engagements that were, in practice, month-to-month (really 60 days with the cancellation notification period). But both Alex and the sales guys had played the terms by ear to sign certain clients over the years. He wasn't sure how many "exceptions to the rule" there were or how to easily get this info.

A buyer might not like this inconsistency, Alex realized. And while he had modeled A&S's deals off both trial and error and what he knew about industry best practices, he wasn't sure what Frank's contracts looked like. *Is our escape clause too easy? We've had some clients leave, but I've never raked them over the coals based on anything in the contract. Is Frank going to view this as a weakness?*

Alex put that out of his mind. Frank would view it as a far brighter red flag if Alex couldn't answer the question quickly and casually.

He looked through the accounting files stored on a shared drive. Alex couldn't find a convenient summary of contract terms in the account roll-up spreadsheet that that Acacia updated regularly. Then, he started going through each of the client folders stored in the drive. Some of the folders had signed scanned or digital contracts, but others didn't. And the few agreements he spot-checked were inconsistent, with different formats, lengths, and names.

Alex was simultaneously alarmed and a little relieved by this discovery. He was annoyed that no one maintained the folders with this fundamental info. But if all the contracts *had* been there, it would have taken a great deal of time to compile their terms.

This is sloppy. We're going to need to clean this up before any sale. Hell, we need to clean it up anyway. I don't even know exactly what is going on with all our clients.

Alex considered the possibility that his ignorance was the problem. Acacia was usually on point with this stuff, and there may be a system in place he didn't know about. But to figure that out and answer Frank's question, Alex was going to have to ask her.

He typed a response to Frank:

> No problem. I'm a little busy with a new client meeting this afternoon [...]

Might as well flex a little, Alex thought.

> [...] but I'll get you that summary first thing tomorrow.

⁖𐂷⤸#

Alex walked into Acacia's office, and she looked up from her computer.

"Hey Acacia—got a minute?"

"Of course. What's up," answered A&S's bookkeeper and all-around administrative manager.

"So, I was doing some projections and looking for a list of our clients by contract but can't find the info. Do we have a list of the contract terms, and if so, where does this live?"

Acacia cocked her head and pursed her lips.

"Well … as far as what they're paying every month, that's in our billing system that rolls up into QuickBooks. The rest of the terms are in the contracts themselves."

"And where are those?"

Acacia waved Alex over, pointed to her monitor, and navigated to the accounting folder within the shared drive.

"Most of them are in here," she said.

"Most of them?"

"Well, some of the early contracts before my time were done on paper and haven't been scanned and uploaded, I don't think. They should all be in there." She pointed to a file cabinet. Alex winced when he heard the word "should."

"What do you need them for?" said Acacia. "If you tell me what you're projecting, I can do it for you."

"Nah, that's not necessary," Alex said quickly. "I'm just playing around with some numbers and want to assess where we are at. It seems like we should fundamentally know the nature of all our contracts. I assume most of them are one year with an SLA out and a notification period, but I know some accommodations were made over the years."

"Yes, you guys played it loose on some of the deals. For example, I think there are a few trial periods in there that were never transferred over to anything more substantial," Acacia said. "Bottom line: what do you need? I'll put something together."

"Just compile a list of all of our clients with the contract duration, the basic terms for ending the arrangement, and the charges," Alex answered. "And longer term, we should have this info all in one place and any old contracts updated and scanned. God, I hope they are all signed, and the terms are current."

"Ok. By Friday work?"

Alex paused. He believed he needed to provide a summary

quickly, and an end-of-week deadline probably wouldn't cut it.

"Actually, I'm kind of held up on doing these projections without the info," he said. "If you're not working on anything crucial, is it possible to get this by tomorrow?"

Acacia looked at him squarely for a beat, appraising him and the request.

"I can help out if you can point me in the right direction," Alex added sheepishly.

"I'll see what I can do," she said.

Alex thanked her and headed back to his office. Acacia was very smart. This fact, along with her natural reserve, usually made him wonder what was going on in her head. It was unlikely that she suspected a sale, and Alex hadn't given the impact on his employees a lot of thought, other than his desire to keep the firm as intact as possible. But a little anxiety about what he would tell his people—and when—crept into his thoughts.

More worrisome was what he discovered about his financials and some of the admin systems. The lack of quick visibility into the contract terms and the fact that some of them were still on a piece of paper squirreled away in a filing cabinet were concerning. This pointed to other potential issues. What accounting systems, customer management processes, or other things weren't as dialed in as Alex assumed?

He thought back to some of the business books and blog articles he'd read on the importance of exit planning years ago, along with the routine admonishments from his CPA. "Plan ahead to set your company up for a sale, long before you sell it," was the gist.

Well, that ship has sailed, Alex thought ruefully. *But we still have some time to get our house in order.*

Besides, a lot of small businesses have these problems, and A&S has a very healthy client list and revenue. The checks are clearing every month. And who knows, Frank's firm probably deals with these same issues.

Comforted by the possibility, Alex put aside the misgivings and refocused on work.

꙳ ⌇ ✣

Acacia put the summary together and delivered it to Alex the following morning. As he'd feared, two contracts with longtime clients were missing in action, several needed an update, and a few more had inconsistent terms. Seven contracts weren't even signed. Alex faced a decision: get all the contracts solidified and risk rocking the boat or let sleeping dogs lie since the payments were there. He certainly didn't want to lose any clients and revenue right before an offer.

But these agreements needed to be straightened out, sale or not. So, he told Dani, A&S's account manager, to present new contracts to the clients on their next scheduled check-in calls. They'd frame the issue as a standard renewal of terms, which each one basically was. Alex also asked Acacia to get all digital copies stored in a central location on the drive and sort out some of the other administrative issues he'd discovered. By mid-afternoon, Alex provided a high-level summary of the contract terms to Frank that was essentially accurate but downplayed any problems.

Later that afternoon, Alex dialed up Mike, his agent at the business brokerage, for their scheduled meeting.

"Hey Alex, how are you? Getting excited about this deal? I think we've got a solid prospect here."

"It seems interesting," Alex responded. "I have a few questions, though. We can get into those after you pass along your requests."

"Nah, you go ahead," said Mike. "What's on your mind?"

"Well, I was mainly wondering what the buyer intends to do with the business. Is he going to merge it basically intact, or does he just want our clients?"

"Well, we're not far enough down the path yet," Mike responded. "But the buyer said that he wants to expand. I know he really respects your company and sees it as a great way to do that."

That was a non-answer, thought Alex.

"I see. When is our scheduled intro meeting?"

"We can set that up early next week. I'll send you over some days and times," the agent said.

Alex knew this short meeting would probably be the only one he had with that prospective buyer before a deal went further and became exclusive. The broker had kept the two parties at arm's length and handled all the preliminary due diligence. *Makes sense, I guess. They're protecting their sale.*

Mike then went over his new list of questions about the business, which again centered on clients and profit. They were also less detailed and probing than Frank's requests, though one ask did involve basic client contract terms.

"So, how are we looking?" Alex asked tentatively. "You say the guy respects my company and views it as an opportunity. Do you think they'll make an offer, and would it be a good one?"

"Oh yeah, I'm pretty confident on this one," said Mike. "You can never say a deal is a lock, and we still have a lot of work to do if he gives you a letter of intent. But things are looking really good, and I personally think your companies and goals are a great fit."

After brushing up on 'selling a business 101,' Alex knew that a letter of intent (LOI) was sort of like crossing the Rubicon. He would get a proposal with a concrete number and have a short time to sign it. Once Alex signed an LOI, he'd have to cut off any negotiations with anyone else for a significant period, probably months. Alex was attempting to juggle the two prospects so the offers came in around the same time. But that was hard to control.

"Great. What about the details they've asked for?" Alex said. He hesitated to clarify the question for a second before deciding to push forward. Alex didn't want to project any weakness, but he really wanted this information. Besides, this broker was just as interested in selling A&S as Alex was.

"You're my broker, and you've done this probably a hundred times. Any issues with the financials or other info that the buyer might not like?"

"I haven't seen any red flags," Mike responded. "The contracts and clients look about par for the course in your industry, though we'll get into that deeper after an LOI. You've got a solid client list and healthy revenue, and that means a lot."

"What about the offer and multiplier? Do you think those will be 'par for the course' in my industry, too? Five times profit—or more—going to happen?" Alex said with an insecure chuckle.

"Totally possible; you've got a strong asset!" Mike said. "Again, we'll see what comes down with an LOI. But I am confident that any offer will be a good one, and you are going to like the number."

Alex ended the call with a smile on his face.

Anticipation

THE DAYS CRAWLED BY AS Alex subconsciously put many of his management duties on autopilot. He attended the meetings, conducted the client calls, and chimed in on the operational problems but made no decisions that would significantly affect the company—and there *were* a few in the queue that should be made. Alex stalled for time by giving his team vague excuses. And he winced when Mekhi took the initiative to present a preliminary roadmap for Digital Shield.

Alex hadn't volunteered a word about buying the cybersecurity platform in almost a month. He'd almost forgotten about the initiative, assuming his team had written it off as 'another annoying distraction from the boss.' But Mekhi, spurred by loyalty, guilt, or diligence, had surprised Alex by crafting a detailed implementation and training proposal. The plan targeted a full implementation within eight months, outlining the resources A&S needed or could reroute toward the project. It was excellent work that obviously took a lot of time.

"Thank you, Mekhi. This is amazing," Alex said with a stab of guilt. *Where was this guy a month or two ago?* he added silently.

Alex worried about a sale's impact on A&S's employees every so often, but it wasn't what dominated his thoughts. Instead, he experienced a strange yet familiar feeling in the pit of his stomach that was hard to describe. It mixed a little anxiety with more excitement and hope, almost like how he'd felt as a kid before the first day of school—maybe combined with anticipating Christmas morning.

But the feeling was more subtle than that. It would occasionally rise up and overtake Alex, and he'd find himself unconsciously frowning or smiling. But for the most part, it was just there, lurking in the background. He knew that something was probably coming—*soon*—that could change his life. But Alex had to pretend it wasn't—and that he didn't care. *Run the company. Hope for the best but be ready for disappointment. Stay cool. Keep it steady.*

These silent mantras helped a little. But the emotions still elbowed their way into Alex's head, and the hope usually won out over worry. Complicating this roller coaster was the fact that he couldn't speak to anyone about any of it for most of the day. Fortunately, Alex's wife took up the slack with 'domestic therapy' duty.

Alex's attempts to stay cool had mixed results, especially at home. But Kristi's pragmatic side usually dominated her perspective. They inevitably talked about the future, including what they'd do for a living, where they'd live, how to use and invest the money, and some of the exciting places they could travel to with the kids. But Kristi would inevitably reel Alex back toward reality, reminding him that there wasn't even an offer yet—and when there was, he didn't know what it would be. A mildly chastened Alex would agree and dial it back a little. Nevertheless, he was confident enough in his company and his conversations with the prospects to believe at least one offer would be a good one.

"Have you really considered the minimum you'll take for the company? And at this point, what it would take for you to walk away from a deal?" Kristi pressed him during one of their dinner-time talks.

"Sure," Alex responded casually. But then he paused and honestly thought about it.

"I think we might get $2 million, and that's sort of an ideal number in my head," he said. "But it might be a little more or less. As for the minimum I'd take, well, the average multiple of profits for most strong businesses is a little over three, I think, and that's about $1.3 million for A&S. But strong businesses and MSPs specifically go for more; say, five- or even six-times profit. So that's like $2 to $2.4 mill."

"Ok, so what would it take for you to walk away?" Kristi insisted. "Hate to say it, my dear, but with the way you're talking, you are pretty much sold on selling." Alex frowned.

"I don't know. $1.8, maybe? $1.7?" he said. "We'll have to see what happens. You're the one who keeps saying we need to see the offer."

"That's true," Kristi said with a laugh. "I'm just reminding you to be ready for it since you said you'll have a pretty short amount of time to decide."

"I'm with you on this," she continued. "We'll make this decision together, and I trust your judgment. And I'm excited—I really am. It just doesn't seem real yet, and we have to keep an open mind."

Alex kissed and hugged her, thanking his lucky stars he'd met this woman on a blind date 16 years ago. She was right, of course. He should stay focused and realistic. But there was nothing wrong with a little excitement. Further, Alex was almost certain two offers were coming soon, and at least one of them would be good enough.

He'd spent 18 years building his business, and A&S had become a significant player in his area. The company had been an early adopter of monthly recurring revenue and the MSP model, developing solid systems and processes to make it work. He had the clients, revenue, tech, and people. It was a healthy business and, therefore, a valuable one. And when he thought of all those years of struggle, including coming out the other side of multiple crises stronger, the value only grew in Alex's head.

I took the risks, put in the effort, and built something great. Now, it's time for me to cash in.

He once again thought about what he could do with a couple of million dollars and how his life would change. No more worrying about the business and what he needed to do for it to survive and grow. No more being responsible for so many people and clients. Things were looking good, and a sale was probably going to happen at the right price.

He was going to be secure. And free.

The Reality Check

A LEX'S HEART SKIPPED A BEAT when he saw the subject line. The letter of intent (LOI) to buy his business was here.

Frank had said the letter was coming a few days ago, and Alex was glad his old professional acquaintance had the first crack at buying the company. After a meeting with the other potential buyer and receiving more questions from him through the business brokerage, Alex's suspicions about the guy only wanting his clients had grown. In contrast, he believed Frank would run A&S like another branch of his firm and keep the business intact. Most of Alex's employees would probably keep their jobs, and his clients would be served.

Alex clicked on the attachment and felt an odd thrill reading the words "Private and Confidential" at the top. Predictably, the text was filled with legal jargon that made it hard to get through, such as "pursuant to," "thereto," and "subject to." He quickly internalized the standard but annoying legalese word key: he was the "**Seller**," Frank was the "**Buyer**," they were both "**Parties**," and "**Acquired Assets**" basically meant his business. There were about a dozen more bolded definitions as he went through the letter.

Alex forced himself to be patient and read the entire five-page document from the top. The first section explained the overall intent to buy, along with the key definitions. The second section outlined how the transaction would work, but it certainly wasn't plain English, and he only understood most of it. IRS forms, for example, would be left to the accountant.

Alex was midway through the third section, the eight-point list of "**Purchased Assets**," before he lost his cool and looked for *the number*.

It was all the way down in a sixth section titled "Compensation." Alex quickly grasped that he would receive only $400,000 at closing. Reading further, the rest was $1,200,000 in installments over ... 36 months.

$1.6 million—is that it? And only 400k up front?

Alex furiously scanned the document, looking for other back-end payments. He didn't find any. Instead, he absorbed some of the terms of those installments, which were paid monthly and contingent on the performance of the company over three years. Alex became slightly alarmed and more frustrated, the latter because the section and its terms were nearly inscrutable.

He understood that the payouts were based on maintaining clients and monthly recurring revenue, and that project revenue was classified and paid differently. Essentially, he'd get a fixed cut of A&S's monthly revenue after the sale. But all the math—specifically the conditions for getting paid less—wasn't sinking in. He couldn't quickly evaluate whether it was fair.

I have to pay a lawyer and an accountant just to explain this to me in plain English. Overcomplicated, so one of their law school buddies on the other side of the table gets paid to figure it out. What a racket.

Alex knew this was ungenerous. Good agreements were precise. But he was a little cross with the number and that the vast majority of it was a three-year earn-out. And the complicated document seemed to obscure the real story.

They're only paying me $1.6 million. And maybe not all of that.

This figure was only a four-times multiple of A&S's profit. After his research over the past few weeks, Alex knew this was reasonable for many businesses but less than some averages for IT managed services providers he'd read about. Many MSPs achieved multiples of six or more, and Alex had assumed he'd get at least a multiple of four-and-a-half or five.

Alex's shoulders slumped and he closed his eyes. The offer was less than he'd hoped, though he could certainly live on that money. But A&S was a successful business built over almost two decades of intense effort; maybe not his blood, but his sweat and tears were certainly part of the firm. A&S had more than 60 clients, strong profits, a great team, and excellent service. How all of this didn't end up in an industry-average value mystified Alex. He wondered if he was being lowballed or just missing something key.

After making it through the rest of the LOI, three more things bothered him. First, Frank planned to keep Alex on as an employee, for a period "to be determined prior to closing." Second, part of the employment section included "retaining two key employees" for at least one year. Finally, he only had a week to sign the document.

Alex straightened up and shook his head. The letter was what it was, and now was time to act.

The first order of business was to get this LOI in the hands of his accountant and lawyer, so they could evaluate it and spell out the details *quickly*. Then, he needed to light a fire under the business brokerage to try and get a competing LOI from the other buyer before the week was up. Once he signed this document—*if* he signed it—any other deals would be cut off for months.

Finally, he'd either have to push back on this offer, not sign it, or at least hopefully get a good reason it was different than expected.

∴'҈∌͵⫞#

Alex's attorney reviewed the contract within 24 hours, and the breakdown was equal parts comforting and alarming. On the plus side, the lawyer said that none of the terms were unusual or underhanded, though they certainly focused on mitigating the buyer's risk by tying so much of the payout to performance. The attorney also said that Alex's one-week deadline to sign was "relatively generous, as a lot of agreements only give you a day or two."

But the earn-out details that confused Alex were a little disturbing when the attorney clarified them. Alex would receive a percentage of the business's revenue after the sale in 36 monthly installments that ideally added up $1.2 million. The contract projected A&S's monthly revenue based on the firm's current numbers but was slightly more conservative. If A&S had a bad year and didn't hit those benchmarks, Alex's monthly payment would be reduced accordingly.

Worse, if the business earned less than anticipated in the first 12 months, the last two years of payments would be reduced and benchmarked again to the shortfall. The bottom line was that A&S's continued success was key, and its performance during that first year was huge.

This made Alex revise his initial hesitance about an employment contract—though he ultimately came to the same conclusion about it.

His motivation for selling was to break free from the grind *and* the worry about ensuring A&S succeeded in a competitive and rapidly changing industry. This lengthy earn-out period and his continued employment meant that freedom probably wouldn't happen soon. Yes, he could earn the money quicker by selling the business—and he was probably guaranteed more of it—but only by two to three years if A&S did well. And unfortunately, much of the performance anxiety would still be there, only he'd have *less* control.

That said, since so much money depended on the company earning, Alex was glad he would still be involved. He steeled himself to the idea of putting his shoulder into a business he'd mentally checked out of while dreaming about world travel and no deadlines. Alex had known he'd still be on board after the sale to guarantee a smooth transition, but this might be a bigger commitment.

Unfortunately, Alex wasn't the only factor in A&S's success. After signing the non-disclosure agreement, he'd told Frank who his key employees were, highlighting Mekhi and, to a lesser extent (and with reservations), Ron. Alex extolled their value because it was true but also to tout A&S's success and quality team, along with trying to guarantee they'd still have jobs. Now, singing their praises may have come back to bite him.

The sale was contingent on both employees signing "stay" contracts for at least a year. Given the performance-based earn out, Alex knew Mekhi *had to* stay on, as the company would be crippled without him. And if both Ron and Mekhi didn't sign, the sale might not happen at all.

Alex needed to have some difficult conversations soon. It stirred worry about how all his employees would react to him selling the business but especially those key personnel.

How will Mekhi and Ron react? Will they be angry or hurt? And what if they don't play ball with the buyer or the sale? That could kill the deal.

Alex knew Mekhi well enough to know he could have a frank conversation with him. But Mekhi could also be inscrutable sometimes. He *seemed* happy at A&S and certainly liked his job—hell, he was made for it—but that didn't mean he wouldn't have a problem with the sale. Ron was another story. He was a valuable technician and a good project manager, but he was routinely difficult. Alex could see Ron giving him grief before signing any employment contract.

I'll worry about that later. First, I have to figure out if I'm even going to sign this thing.

꙳ ✺ ✦ #

Alex emailed Mike at the business brokerage, notifying him that an interested buyer had made an offer and asking if his client was ready to make a different one. Alex specified that he'd need to know within a few days. Given Mike's annoyingly 'salesy' answers to some of his questions, Alex couldn't help but smile at how the lead broker agent would react to the threat to his commission.

That ought to send him scrambling.

Sure enough, Alex received Mike's quick reply and a promise to get with the interested buyer quickly. He'd also emailed Frank, but not before obsessing over the language in his message. Alex settled on thanking him for the LOI and noting that he had "a few questions." He also got a speedy response, and now it was time to make the call.

Alex took a deep breath, reminded himself to strike an inquisitive and relaxed but firm tone, and hit Frank's number.

"Hey Alex, how are you?"

"Good, man. Thanks again for sending it over the LOI. I have some questions on the offer and some specific terms."

"Shoot."

"Well, first, I'm a little surprised at the overall number," Alex said. "A&S is a strong company with a great team and a healthy client list, and a lot of MSPs sell for more than a multiple of four. Some go for five or six. When we spoke before the LOI, I thought we agreed that we were in the ballpark of five." Alex let the next question hang without asking it.

"Understood, Alex. The basic answer is that we carefully evaluated your business and the numbers, looked at our business, and the offer is what makes sense to us right now," Frank said. He paused for a beat before continuing.

"As for how we achieved that multiple: there's no doubt that A&S is a strong company. You've got a fantastic team, some great clients and processes, and even your technology stack fits with ours really well. Make no mistake: I want to buy your company. I'm excited for the opportunity. But there are a few factors that just pose some risks for us."

"Okay. Such as?" said Alex.

"I think the biggest unknown is the contracts. It seems that a few of them aren't locked down. And of the ones that are, they are almost all one year with a pretty broad and quick out," said Frank. Alex began to speak but Frank continued.

"I know many of these clients have been with you a long time and are happy with the services," he said. "But one client represents a very big chunk of revenue and has been there less than three years. Further, we've transitioned most of our clients to two and even three-year deals, and our SLA escape clause is narrower. We just have a lot more revenue guaranteed for longer."

"I see," was all Alex could muster.

"Again, none of this affects the fact that I want to buy your business, and I really think the clients will stick around. So, I definitely think you'll achieve the earn-out," Frank continued. "But we had to structure the deal so we share the risk a bit."

Frank again stressed his interest in the company and his admiration for what Alex had built, attempting to soothe any hard feelings. But Alex pressed him on whether there were any other factors that influenced the offer. Frank considered these items less pivotal than the contract terms of A&S's clients, but he also mentioned that a "slightly high" portion of revenue was non-recurring, dedicated to projects rather than ongoing services. And he believed that Alex had underpaid himself somewhat relative to what he was "worth as a fantastic CEO."

This factor segued into Alex asking about the nature of his employment contract after the sale; specifically, the possible details of the arrangement. Frank envisioned "up to three years," but really a one-year contract that was renewable every year based on mutual agreement.

"You've done an excellent job, and we know you'll be invaluable integrating the companies," said Frank. "But you'll have the freedom to decide whether you want to continue for longer than a year."

The conversation ended amicably, with Frank again expressing his excitement about the deal, and Alex thanking him and promising to review the LOI closely along with his attorney. He hadn't achieved any changes, but he did have a better idea of why the number was lower than anticipated. The nature of the employment contract was ok; he could bail after a year if the company was on course.

Alex also got a strong feeling that the offer was what it was; it would be difficult to get any concessions. And he wasn't even sure if revisions might be reasonable or achievable, nor what the process was for negotiating between an LOI and closing.

I need some help.

Indecision
and Mourning

ITHIN A DAY, ALEX HAD another offer from the other
potential buyer. The letter of intent sent by the business
brokerage was a completely different animal than the one he'd gotten from Frank.

It was only a one-page document with little legalese. The number was specified quickly and almost matched Frank's but with better
payout terms: Alex would get 40% up front with the remainder paid
over two years, contingent on maintaining a reasonable proportion of
clients and revenue. There were no employment contracts specified,
and the list of "assets to be acquired" was shorter. When Alex sent it
to his lawyer for a professional take, his suspicions were confirmed.

"This guy seems to really want your clients, not necessarily your
whole company," was the attorney's assessment. "The payment terms

are quicker, but you'll have less control over the backend. It may be a better offer if you just want to walk away and be done with it."

Alex felt good about having another option but didn't like the idea of selling off his firm "for parts." And he still wasn't sure what to do.

It was finally time to discuss all of this with his wife. Alex had avoided the topic since he'd received the first offer, which was strange. They usually discussed everything immediately—certainly events that would impact the family. But he put off the talk for a couple of days while getting the other offer and trying to figure out a plan of action. Alex knew Kristi would be supportive, see things pretty objectively, and give good advice. But he couldn't help but think there'd be an uncurrent of "I told you so," given her warnings about getting too excited—even if she never said those words.

That was unfair. It was his own disappointment and the embarrassment about being overconfident that he was avoiding.

Alex texted Kristi, letting her know he had offers and asking to talk. The phone rang almost immediately.

"Two offers? Congratulations, babe! How are they?"

"Good. Okay, maybe? A little less than I'd hoped and with different terms. I'm really not sure what I'm—*we*—are gonna do."

Alex outlined the deals, expressing his worry about the payouts and the company's performance. He explained how staying on for a longer time wasn't ideal in Frank's offer, but he was worried the other buyer would fire all of his people and gut the business.

"I mean, I've built something great, and all of those people are depending on me," Alex said. "The clients and especially the employees. I get the feeling that a lot of people will be canned. How can I sell out and leave everyone in the lurch?"

"That is tough," she said. "But I wouldn't worry so much about the clients, except how they affect the payouts. Remember, a buyer has an incentive to give them good service, too. If not, they'll find another MSP. But your *people*—I understand."

Then, there was the number. Alex winced discussing it, given all the times he'd said they might get $2 million or even more. To her credit, Kristi merely offered that "1.6 is pretty darn good" and asked him whether it made more financial sense to keep the business for a few years.

"But only if you really want to and are up to it," she offered.

"I don't know. Honestly ... I'm starting not to think so," he said. "The funny thing is, I wasn't even thinking of selling—though I know I wasn't enjoying running it anymore. Then, Frank emails. And somehow, my world gets turned upside down within a few weeks, and I just got very attached to the idea."

Kristi chuckled, not unkindly.

"I get it. You see a light at the end of the tunnel, and it looks pretty great," she said. "Look: 1.6 million bucks in three years is still money that most people only dream about. We've got the kids' college taken care of, we already have a decent nest egg, and I've still got a job. We're not even in the ballpark of going hungry, whatever you decide. Quite the opposite!"

"Yeah, but would I be selling out cheap? I mean, what I put into this business ... it's successful, stable, and all those years of work ..."

"No offense, honey but is that an ego thing? I understand the feeling. And you've done an amazing job; I'm really proud of what you've accomplished," Kristi said. "But it's a business—and this *is* business."

"Yeah. But what if I'd be making a mistake?"

"Well, if I understand what you're telling me—and what the lawyer is telling you—I doubt anything you decide will be a huge mistake," Kristi offered. "Even if you miss out on a couple of hundred thousand dollars or something, we'll be fine. And there are other things that are important in life."

"Here's what I think you need to do," she continued. "First, decide whether or not you have the energy to keep going. Then, honestly look at the terms and figure out whether anything is off—like, will A&S hit those numbers? And maybe you should talk to someone who has sold a business before."

Alex had considered this after signing the NDA, and he'd spoken to his cousin who had bought a business but had no experience selling one. Alex was tempted to ask some folks in his industry peer group but stopped short of doing it. He didn't want to let everyone know he was selling in case the deal didn't happen—or any competitors or colleagues caught wind of it and interpreted this as a problem with the business.

"You there?" said Kristi.

"Yeah, sorry, I was just thinking about who I could ask," he said.

"What about Jason?"

Alex thought a moment. "That's not a bad idea. Thanks, Kristi. As usual, your advice—all of it—is good. Let me think on it. I love you."

Jason was someone Alex had considered talking to, but they hadn't spoken for years. He was a friend—maybe a former friend, now—who was something of a mentor in the early days. Alex met the older man when he joined a local leads group while trying to drum up business. They'd hit it off, and Jason provided Alex plenty of tips on how to build and maintain his new company. Jason didn't run an MSP or even any business related to IT—he'd owned shoe stores and now, a retail consultancy—but he was an expert on promotion, hiring, and financials. His help had been invaluable.

While the two men had spoken regularly for years, they'd lost touch over the last five. Jason sold his business—at least, his local one—seven years ago and semiretired to Arizona. He might be the perfect person to give some outside perspective. The man didn't know much about MSPs, but he knew businesses and certainly went through selling a couple. And Alex could speak with him without ringing any bells in the local IT scene.

Nevertheless, Alex felt a little guilty about not staying in touch, and he hesitated to contact Jason now that he needed something. Hell, he'd skipped the man's second wedding—though he did send a gift.

Screw it. He's probably bored down there, anyway. It'll be a good excuse to catch up.

꒰'꒱꒰#

As it turned out, Jason was in town visiting his grandkids. He'd picked up the phone immediately and seemed genuinely happy to hear from Alex. They quickly planned to grab dinner at a local restaurant.

Alex arrived a few minutes late and spotted Jason at the bar. Jason rose from his stool with a smile and gave Alex a hearty handshake. Only minutes into their conversation, Alex was taken aback by the changes in the man.

Jason had always been friendly and had a wicked sense of humor. But his jokes were usually dry, cynical, and based on complaints. He had always seemed like someone "put upon by the world." Now in his sixties, Jason was older and greyer but had lost a lot of weight and seemed happy—like, *oddly* happy.

"It's great to see you," Alex said. "You look great! Seems like retirement agrees with you."

"Oh, I'm not retired," answered Jason. "Retired from owning stores, sure. I've still got a great little consulting gig running."

"Awesome, I'd love to hear about it. Listen, man, I'm sorry about not being able to make it to your wedding. A lot of stuff was going on with the business, and I didn't have time for anything. How's your wife?"

"She's great. Keeps me on my toes. And no worries—I totally understand."

The two men fell into conversation like they'd just seen each other yesterday. Jason told Alex about his life in Arizona and his new version of one of his old businesses, serving as a retail management consultant. He was enthusiastic about the work, noting that he was "born to do it."

"The hours are easier, the job is pretty flexible, and I'm genuinely making a difference," Jason said. "When I help a client figure something out, it feels incredible."

After a detour into how affordable nice houses were in Arizona vs. Philly, Jason steered the conversation back to the evening's main topic. "Now, tell me what's been going on with this business of yours."

Alex's long, unbroken answer was one part stump speech and two parts therapy session. He reviewed how A&S had grown after Jason left Philly before hitting a crisis a few years later. Alex described the long hours spent righting the ship and his hiring, retention, pricing, and operational challenges. He spoke about his latest fears of ransomware and rapid technological change, and whether he had the energy or smarts to keep up. Finally, Alex explained how a nudge from Frank had made him consider a sale, followed by outlining the two buy offers and his reservations with both.

Jason listened patiently and attentively through it all with only a few slight nods, shakes of his head, and raised eyebrows. When Alex finally stopped speaking, Jason looked at him squarely and laughed.

"That is a hell of a roller coaster, my friend. It sounds like you've got a big decision on your hands," Jason said. "But I'm pretty sure you already know what you're going to do … even if you don't really *know* it yet."

Alex smiled and looked at him quizzically. "Ok, smart guy. Tell me what I don't know that I know."

"Well, good buddy, I think you're going to sell," Jason said. "You're done. You're tired. You want something new. And while I do believe you should think carefully about it, it sounds like you're *probably* going to take Frank's offer. But one way or another, you're already sold on selling."

"Maybe. But I don't want to sell my business for a song, and I'm not sure if I'm getting underbid or could get screwed on the backend. You've sold what, two businesses now? I mean, are these deals fair?"

"Did you push back on any of the terms?" Jason said.

Alex described his conversation with Frank the other day, explaining how Frank said Alex was underpaying himself and that the contracts weren't long enough.

"Those are pretty standard reasons. On my first sale, the buyer said the same thing about my salary and dinged me for not keeping the business books and my personal accounts separate enough. I didn't focus on monthly recurring revenue in my companies, of course, but the stability of income can impact value. And you should know that the due diligence will only get more intense from here. So, my biggest piece of advice for you isn't completely too late … but it's a *little* late."

"What's that?"

By now, Alex was leaning forward and literally sitting on the edge of his seat.

"Well … for one thing, a lot of these informal discussions about the number should have happened before you got that LOI," Jason said. "Did you talk about how much?"

"I'd mentioned a five times multiple of profit, and Frank said we were in the ballpark," said Alex. "The business broker did, too."

"And the employment contract?"

"I said that I'd be willing to stay on to help with a smooth transition, but I didn't say three years or anything."

"Ok," Jason said as he clasped his fingers and drummed his thumbs against each other. He paused before continuing.

"Well, I'm sure you know that business sales should ideally be planned well in advance. After some of the surprises I experienced with my first sale, I applied those lessons to my next business. One was that I tightened the financials and ops up, trying to run it like I might sell it tomorrow. But another was that I made a list of things that I needed right before the next sale. Not in my head, mind you. I actually thought about it and wrote those things down."

"What was on the list?"

"The first thing was the number I would be willing to accept—and at least half up front," Jason said. "Another was no employment contract. But those things were unique to what I wanted and the situation my business was in at the time. I knew it's value, the market, and the buyers, so I knew I had a good chance—or at least a reasonable one—of getting those things."

"Those specifics aren't important for you," he continued. "What is important is listing out the absolute non-negotiables that you'll commit to during the process. Ideally, after you've sat down with your family and before someone who is interested hits you with an LOI. It ensures you don't get so emotionally wrapped up in a sale that you give too much away."

"Smart," Alex said with a sigh. "And yeah, maybe a little late to do that."

"It's ok, man. Not totally too late," Jason said with a smile. "You should still make a list, even if you sign one of those LOIs. The due diligence process may create new challenges, and the deal isn't done until it's done. But yeah, in a perfect world, some of your concerns would have been clarified and addressed after you signed those NDAs. From what you told me, though, it doesn't sound like either of these offers is too bad."

"I just … I'm just not sure if I'd be letting it go too easily," Alex said. "All that work. And it's a successful MSP with a great track record. What if I could get more?"

Jason chuckled.

"You probably could get more if you search hard enough for the right buyer. Especially if you don't sign, lengthen some of the contracts, and make a few other adjustments to prep it for a sale," he said. "But that will take a little time and effort, and you'd have to walk away from what's on the table. You've got to decide how important the extra money is and whether you've got that fight in you."

"And the economy could go south … or the business," said Alex.

"Always. And nowadays, most businesses sold have *some* significant earn-out period on the backend. Buyers want to share the risk," Jason said. "The other thing I'll point out is that *you're* wrapped up in it, the business. It's your baby, and I know the feeling—I've had a few of my own. It's hard to let go and maybe harder to think it's not worth what you think it's worth, given all of that work. But in the end, a buyer is going to pay what a buyer is going to pay. You can influence the number a bit, but it's only really worth what *they* think it is, without any of that emotion you're feeling. I mean, at least as far as any deals on the table go."

"Yeah, you're right," Alex offered. "Thanks, Jason."

"I understand the indecision," added Jason. "Just figure out if you want to keep running the business. If you do, move on from the offers and move forward. If not, think about an offer and what kind of impact a buyer will have on A&S—and decide whether you can live with it."

✧⁘✦#

Alex awoke the next day with a clear head, despite having a mild hangover. He spoke with Kristi before going into work late, and the talk only reinforced a decision he'd already made. Jason's advice had been invaluable, allowing Alex some distance from his emotions. But just as eye-opening was seeing his old friend and learning about his life. The man had moved on to something new and seemed like a different person. A happier, more fulfilled one.

Alex hadn't felt that way in years. It was time for something new. And while he could accept selling the business, he couldn't live with selling out his people.

He signed Frank's letter of intent and emailed it.

Guilt

June 1st–June 10th

THE CLOCK STARTED TICKING ONCE Alex signed the letter of intent. The closing date for the purchase was 60 days away, and there was a lot to do. Frank and Alex set up a meeting with their respective attorneys and accountants to kick off the due diligence. Further, Frank specified he needed an auditor to examine the business's books, systems, and processes, which required at least one visit to A&S. And this called for a cover story.

In all of Alex's research on selling a business, one piece of advice rarely changed: don't tell employees until the deal is complete unless they are key personnel who need to sign stay agreements. The reason was compelling: people may react in ways that could scuttle the deal. Employees might panic or become resentful. Some will immediately start looking for new jobs, and many individuals will ease up on their work, tanking productivity. After all, what's the point of killing yourself if the business won't exist soon (at least, in its present form), and you might not have a job?

Alex recognized the irony. The biggest factor in making his business successful and attracting a buyer—the people—could be the biggest threat to a sale. And while he understood the logic of keeping employees in the dark, he didn't like it one bit.

Alex thought he was a pretty good leader, and he was self-aware enough to know that one of his leadership strengths could also be a weakness. He'd always had a style now becoming vogue among business gurus who do TED talks: transparency and vulnerability. When A&S was doing well, his people knew it. And when the firm faced challenges—even existential ones, as the company had a few years ago—his people also knew that. Alex had always been open about the good and bad, almost to a fault.

This trait had probably bitten him in the ass once or twice when an employee left for a better opportunity. But overall, the leadership style had worked and even paid dividends. The team members who'd been with Alex through the rough times trusted him, and he trusted them in turn. A core of employees proved their worth by powering through challenges, and they believed he would always shoot them straight. But now, he *had to* lie to them. All of them.

Alex took a deep breath and walked into the conference room for A&S's weekly leadership meeting. Mekhi, Ron, Kevin, Acacia, and Dani were already there.

"Hey guys," Alex said. "Sorry for being late. Let's get started."

The meeting followed its usual routine, with each individual summarizing their weekly objectives and progress toward last week's goals. Ron had finished a necessary hardware upgrade for a longtime client. Acacia's numbers update showed the MSP was on course. Freed up from the ransomware attack recovery, Mekhi was making headway on the queue of client services. Dani spoke about some marketing initiatives that all sounded good, though Alex still wasn't convinced of their value. And surprisingly, Kevin had made a big sale, bringing in one of those "whales" he was always talking about. In truth, it was a pretty standard account—an accounting firm with three locations—but it was a victory, nonetheless.

"Great job, Kevin!" said Alex with a smile. "Now, keep that up and sign three more just like it!"

And hopefully, we'll keep all of them for three years, he added silently.

When it was his turn to speak, Alex plowed through his standard update before getting to the main thing on his mind.

"FYI guys, I am bringing in a consultant to examine our processes, books, just about everything," he said. "His name is Cam, and he's going to be doing an audit. I don't think this will impact anything you're doing much, as all of his requests will go through me. But please be aware that he'll be here next week, and I may ask you for things. And, you know, just be nice to him."

"Who is he, again? And why is he doing an audit?" Acacia said.

Alex had assumed Acacia would be the first to respond, as the bookkeeper might feel territorial.

"He's an expert with a business consulting firm," Alex said. "He'll take a look at how we're doing things to see if there are any weaknesses. You know we had some issues with unsigned and inconsistent contracts—"

Alex hurriedly continued when he saw Acacia's eyes narrow slightly.

"—which is my fault, and the sales team's fault over about a decade. We played things by ear to get clients in the door. But anyway, he's going to be looking at stuff like that to see if there's anything else we need to shore up."

Alex winced inwardly. The visitor sort of *was* a consultant who was looking for issues. But there was no way around giving them *a reason* he was consulting, and that had to be a lie.

"Will he be looking at our client-facing stuff," asked Mekhi.

"The focus is on the books, but I may have a question or three for you on anything ops-related," Alex said. "Again, I don't think this will disrupt anybody much. I just wanted you to know that a stranger will be in the office, and I may have a few asks while he's here."

Announcing the visitor would head off many questions, especially as the news trickled down from the leadership team to everyone else. But it wouldn't stop all speculation; people liked to talk. Hopefully, the cover story would be accepted at face value. Bringing in a consultant wasn't unusual at many businesses, but it was odd at A&S. Alex quickly moved on by asking Kevin more about the new client.

⁓ ☙ ⸙ #

The next 10 days passed quickly but not painlessly.

Cam visited A&S headquarters to look at the books and processes, meeting with Alex to provide his list of requests. Predictably, there were some items that Alex couldn't easily find, and he had to ask Acacia, Dani, and Kevin for their help. Every time Alex needed something, he felt a twinge of guilt while prepping a small cover story. Fortunately, he never needed to use the lies; everyone just provided what he needed. But Acacia did ask some clarifying questions about the deliverables, and he felt like she could see through him each time.

Alex was on autopilot as he ran the business, and it was a strange feeling. While he'd become tired over the years and occasionally burned out, he'd always remained engaged. Now, he felt like he did in the last month of his senior year of high school, or the two weeks' notice after quitting a job. Alex worked hard on anything related to the sale, showed up for meetings, and dealt with his team's questions and challenges. But he made no unnecessary decisions and politely stiff-armed both Mekhi and Ron when they brought up avoidable projects.

"I'm focused on some of our improvements," was the excuse if they pressed him. But Alex sensed Mekhi was slightly hurt at shelving the Digital Shield project. And rejecting a client's major technology upgrade completely confused Ron.

"But … they need it," Ron argued.

"Well, they don't need it this minute," Alex responded. "It will be a major upfront cost and a lot of work. Let me sort out some other things before we get into it. They'll be fine for the time being."

A&S's bewildered project manager nodded and walked out of Alex's office with a grunt. Alex didn't always see eye to eye with Ron, but he still felt guilty keeping the secret. And there was another emotion when he thought about the grumpy project manager: fear.

The sale looked on track, and Alex had made peace with the number and the terms of the deal. He was even a little excited about signing on the dotted line. This excitement had grown when Frank said that Alex's duties during the post-sale employment contract would be "flexible," depending on how the integration went and if the company was on track.

One thing that remained inflexible, however, was the stay agreement that Ron and Mekhi had to sign. Alex tried to underplay Ron's importance a bit in recent conversations, but Frank didn't seem to take the hint and certainly didn't alter the terms. In truth, Alex was merely laying the groundwork for the possibility Ron balked when he was told about the sale. Alex also worried about Mekhi's reaction—but there was little he could do about that. Mekhi *was* a truly essential employee.

If he walks—heck, if either of them does—there probably won't be a sale. And I could be left with a crippled company and no buyer.

Alex needed to speak with both men very soon, and his fears would be resolved one way or another. But the guilt over the rest of the team would continue until closing.

Alex was particularly worried about Acacia, Dani, and, to a lesser extent, Kevin. Frank signaled his intent to "keep the shop whole" but made no guarantees, and nothing was specified in writing. Alex knew that Frank would probably keep all the technicians since good ones were hard to find. And as the account manager, Dani would probably be valuable—at least, initially. But A&S's bonus structure that had stopped turnover cut into the bottom line, and Alex could see the new owner replacing some less-critical roles.

Successful salespeople—especially local ones—were usually

immune to restructuring after a business sale. But Kevin *wasn't* particularly successful. And no matter how Alex gamed it, he believed Acacia's position was on the chopping block. Frank's company had its own financial manager and systems. Accountants and bookkeepers were almost always redundant during a merger, and they were often the first to go.

Alex wasn't close with Acacia; she was too inscrutable for that. But she'd worked for him a long time, and he considered her A&S's most reliable asset besides Mekhi. Acacia did her work efficiently, consistently, and without complaint. She'd suggested some innovative account changes along with improving A&S's financial tracking and processes. So, while Alex had a big payday coming after his years of hard work, hers might end up in a pink slip.

That's not all she's gotten. I've provided a job, a good work environment, and pretty good pay and benefits for a decade, he told himself.

The guilt always won out over the rationalizations, however. And no matter how bad the pit in Alex's stomach got, the advice from everyone was the same: do not tell employees who are not part of the deal until the ink is dry. Alex had even called his former mentor Jason, who always preached that "good people are everything" in a business, to get his perspective.

"Don't do it!" Jason blurted out as Alex was sharing his guilt. "I get it, and I've been there. But you are the boss. You are a business owner, and this is business. It's part of the game. If you tell employees, they'll quit or sandbag their work before closing. So, if you're worried about numbers tanking after the deal, you should worry ten times more about what could happen before it's done."

"I know. It's still hard to lie to them," Alex offered.

"First: you're not lying. You're simply only telling them what they need to know right now," Jason explained. "Second, while some people might lose their jobs, it sounds like most won't. And you won't be able to guarantee anyone anything right now anyway if you tell them. People will just worry right up until it changes hands, when the new owner clarifies things. You're really not doing anyone any favors, including yourself. It might ease the guilt a little, but it could also destroy the deal."

"But—"

"Don't do it!"

Alex sighed. He knew it was good advice, even if he hated following it.

Coming Clean,
Part 1

June 11th

Alex parked his car in front of the sushi restaurant and headed in to have lunch with Mekhi. He'd told his director of operations they needed to take separate cars, as he had "some errands to do afterward." In truth, Alex didn't want to field any questions on the ride over. He wanted Mekhi's full attention and to look his managed services director in the eyes as he gave him the news.

"God, I love this place," said Mekhi after the two men sat down and ordered. Alex smiled. The restaurant choice had been strategic, too. "Now, what's up? You said you had something you wanted to discuss."

"Well, I've got some big news, and you will be the first at A&S to know. So, I have to ask for your discretion," Alex said. Mekhi nodded.

"I'm selling the business."

Mekhi's eyes widened a little.

"Whoa. That *is* big news," Mekhi said. "Why? And to *who?*"

"Frank, who runs an MSP over by Princeton, is the buyer," Alex said. "You briefly met him at that conference a couple of years ago."

"The guy who always had a drink in his hand?"

Alex mentally winced. "Yeah, that's him. He's a good guy, and he knows how to run an MSP. As to why I'm selling: honestly, I just think it's time. I've been running this shop for almost 20 years, and I'm getting a little old and tired. As to why I'm telling you: I'm letting you know early because you are an essential employee, and you are guaranteed a job in the new company. In fact, you're necessary."

"Well … that's good," Mekhi said calmly before sipping his green tea.

Alex launched into an overview of the deal, detailing Frank's intent to keep the shop intact and how Alex had told him that Mekhi was an essential part of the company's success. He explained that Frank wanted Mekhi to sign a stay agreement since he was a critical employee and then covered the basic terms. Frank had prepped Alex with a rough outline of the intended contract, which included a decent raise and a performance-based profit-sharing plan.

"You'll be essential, and if A&S does well over the next couple of years, you'll make a good chunk of change," Alex said. "In fact, you might even be running the place. I think this will work out well for you."

"And you need me to sign as part of the deal," Mekhi observed.

"Yes. Yes, I do," Alex said. "I told him you are essential. And I think you and I both know that I'd need you if I weren't selling, too.

But that's not the only reason I'm hyping up working with Frank. I chose his offer because he wants A&S to continue. I honestly believe this will open up more opportunity for you—including more money—if you sign on with him."

"Well, it sounds good, but I'll have to see whatever he puts in writing," Mekhi said. Alex breathed a sigh of relief. He was surprised at how unfazed Mekhi was by the news.

"What about you? What are you going to do? I know you said you're tired of running things—but why? Is the business at all in trouble?"

"No. And you'd know it if A&S were in trouble," Alex said. He paused for a few seconds; he wanted to be careful about what he shared. Alex wanted to tell Mekhi all his fears about the industry and how A&S would need to innovate to grow. But that wouldn't do anyone any good. So instead, he repeated that he just didn't have the gas to run things anymore, and A&S needed engaged and energetic leadership.

"You are one of those leaders; perhaps *the* leader," Alex said. "I'm not selling because the company is doing poorly, and I'm not leaving it in the lurch. I want to move on because it's time, and I'm leaving it in good hands. There is no way A&S would be where it is without you, and I made sure Frank knows that. And whatever you decide: thank you for doing everything you've done for A&S and me."

"You're welcome," Mekhi said, smiling slightly. "Thanks for the job and the promotions; it's all been great. Tough, but great. I'm not gonna lie: this is a huge surprise. I'll need to process this and hammer out the details of the new position in writing. But as long as I'm gaining salary and the position doesn't change 180 degrees, I'm interested."

"Awesome," Alex said with visible relief.

"Now, I'm going to order more sushi. And you are paying for all of it."

Alex smiled. *That went way easier than I'd expected. One down ... one to go.*

⸫'⟡⟋ #

Alex was riding high that afternoon after the talk with Mekhi. There had been none of the anger or sorrow or accusations of betrayal he'd rehearsed responses to in his mind. At a minimum, Mekhi should have been annoyed by the work he'd done planning for the Digital Shield project while Alex had made excuses for shelving it. But Mekhi was onboard, and the most critical piece of the deal was in place.

An email—followed by a call with Alex's CPA and attorney—brought him back down to earth. Frank's financial auditor Cam had kept digging into A&S's numbers and periodically asking for new ones. He was slowly building financial schedules that would determine the final agreement, including accounts payable, accounts receivable, and cash on hand. And unfortunately, he'd uncovered a hole in the balance sheet.

A&S had recently completed a project for a client involving a major hardware upgrade. And while the client had paid and the servers and switches were installed, A&S still hadn't paid the distributor for the new equipment. The company—and ultimately, Alex—was responsible for $40,000. It remained to be seen whether A&S's cash balance would cover all outstanding debts when the company changed hands. If not, any money owed would come out of Alex's pay-off.

Alex asked his accountant why this had happened but didn't receive a good answer. The issue stemmed from the business's internal financial processes, and Alex wasn't about to raise hell over it with any employees. The money wasn't the end of the world, but Frank was less than two weeks into due diligence.

What else might be hiding in those schedules that will come back to bite me?

This fresh worry became full-blown anxiety that evening. Alex took Ron to dinner to discuss the stay agreement and nail down the last contract essential to the deal. And the conversation didn't go as well as the first one. A&S's project manager was shocked and a little angry.

"I *knew* something was going on!" Ron said accusingly. "All those upgrades we needed that you wouldn't approve. I suppose the new owner will be on the hook for them?"

"Yes, the new owner will have to pay for them, but that's not the reason I delayed those decisions," Alex responded calmly. "A portion of the deal is based on performance after the sale, so I have no interest in leaving the company with a bad ROI. When you sell a business, you just can't make any big decisions that alter its financials. That's 'selling a business 101.' My hands have been a little tied, so we've been in a holding pattern."

The answer mollified Ron but not for long. He peppered Alex with more questions: How long had he been selling it? Why hadn't he told anyone? Was the company in trouble? How many people would be fired?

Alex patiently fielded each question and explained that Ron was considered an essential employee. Then, he broached the stay agreement and its general terms. Once Ron grasped that he was crucial to the deal, his surprise and annoyance were replaced by confidence—and some greed.

"Well, I really need to think hard about this. I'm not totally opposed to it, but this is a big change, and that transition is not going to be easy," Ron said. Alex could almost see the wheels turning in his head.

"I'll need a pretty good raise," Ron added. "Honestly, I think I'm overdue for one anyway."

"I see. What are you thinking, numbers-wise?"

"Twenty-five more a year," Ron responded after a pause. "Along with a good profit-sharing plan."

Oh shit.

Alex froze and willed himself to project calm. Twenty-five grand a year was a hefty sum, especially multiplied over the three-year payout period, and Frank might add that to the balance sheet. Further, Alex had no idea if he even had the power to negotiate, so he resisted the urge to hammer out a deal.

I've got to catch my breath. And if I push too hard, he's really going to know he has me over a barrel.

"Well? What do you think?" Ron said.

"Honestly, Ron, that's a lot of money, and I'll have to think about it," Alex said. He stalled by speculating on Ron's role in the new company and the growth opportunities it presented.

"That all sounds great, but who knows what will happen with a new owner," Ron insisted. "I will need a raise to feel secure."

"I understand your position," Alex said, enunciating the words carefully and pushing down the frustration rising in his gut. "I'll have to run some numbers and give it some thought. You do understand what I said about discretion, right? If anyone knows about the sale, *none of this* is likely to happen."

"Got it. Just please let me know what you think as soon as you run the numbers," Ron said. "You know, this is a big change. I have a lot of uncertainty right now."

Alex caught the subtext.

He might leave. He knows I need him, and he's holding my feet to the fire. Kind of a jerk move but also a smart one. You have to admire it.

Alex decided that he needed to speak openly about this with Frank. Being transparent was the best course of action, even if it signaled another financial weakness. Alex hurried through the rest of his meal while letting Ron steer the rest of the conversation. Within 10 minutes, he called for the check and excused himself, citing family obligations.

◟◞☙↘#

"Hey Frank, we have a slight hiccup," Alex said into the phone the next morning. "One of my people is on board, but the other one is not … yet."

"I see. Which one and what's the issue?" Frank said.

"Mekhi is good to go, pending a review of the contract, and he is the *really* critical employee. But Ron is uncertain about the deal and what will happen with the new company, and he wants a bigger raise."

"How much?"

"$25k a year, and he wants to review any profit-sharing plan."

Frank whistled. "That would … let me see. Yeah, that puts him a lot higher than my own project manager. What do you think of his ask? Did you get a good read on him?"

"Well, he's an asset, but Mekhi is the truly critical employee," Alex said. "I know why he's asking if that's what you mean. It's actually pretty smart, and I understand why he would be uncertain about a new company, a new position, and a new boss. But I'm honestly not sure how we want to handle this or what my authority is to negotiate with him. It will be your shop and your employee."

"Right. Well, thanks for letting me know," Frank said. "Mekhi may be the big catch, but we'll still need a project manager in place to really hit the ground running. With your permission, how about I meet with him to see if I can hammer out an arrangement."

"I think that's a good idea."

Alex didn't love being taken out of the loop, but Frank tackling the problem signaled that it didn't kill the deal—yet, anyway.

The following few weeks brought new issues, new solutions, and new wrinkles to the deal.

Frank successfully negotiated a stay agreement with Ron. They settled on a $15k raise, subject to increase to $20k after the first year based on performance. Alex was pleased that the problem was solved but less happy with the repercussions. Frank politely informed him that because the assumptions had changed, Alex was on the hook for $45k—an assumed $15k raise over three years.

As the process of compiling financial schedules continued, Cam also found more chinks in A&S's armor. One of the MSP's clients, an accounting firm, had prepaid for its annual services in December to reap tax benefits. At closing, there would be five months to go in the contract. This represented $25,000 of services that the new company would be responsible for when A&S changed hands. Unfortunately, Alex had taken that money and spent it, failing to book this unearned revenue properly.

In total, the latest back and forth over the schedules, along with Ron's pay increase, revealed an extra $110,000 in liabilities and a projected cash balance at closing of only about $20,000. That was a $90,000 shortfall that had to come out of Alex's pocket.

On the plus side, reviewing the schedules had revealed some savings for the buyer. But it also unearthed some new expenses for Alex. Like many business owners, he'd paid for personal expenses that were arguably related to the business—such as utilities, home office expenses, and multiple subscriptions—through his company.

The sum was a drop in the bucket compared to the overall deal and A&S's ongoing expenses—it was only about $600 a month. The figure was so small that Frank's people didn't factor it into the numbers on the latest agreement until Alex pushed back and insisted on recouping $7,000 for at least the first year. Frank relented and revised the contract, but Alex's total receivables from the sale would still be $83,000 less than he'd anticipated. Alex also refused to take the hit up front, so the latest contract slightly reduced his back-end payout percentage.

Whereas he'd once dreamed of getting $2 million—or more—for the company and eventually learned to accept 1.6, he was now down to just over 1.5. Bit by bit, the process had chipped away at the company's value, and Alex had to adjust (and readjust) his expectations. These financial wrinkles were unforced errors he'd made while running the business or simply things he hadn't considered. And each time a new issue popped up and he accepted the recalculations, Alex felt like he was giving a piece of himself away—and there was nothing he could do about it.

As Alex's wife and Jason had said months and weeks ago, he had become sold on selling. The financial hits hurt, but none of them were large enough to pull out of the deal. And they paled in comparison to the idea of relieving the burden of running a company.

Alex made peace with it. All of it.

Sheer Panic

July 1st – 25th

THE DEAL APPROACHED CLOSING SMOOTHLY over the next few weeks. The remaining schedules revealed no meaningful surprises as the agreement began to take its final form. Alex kept busy preparing to integrate the companies while planning how and when he would announce the sale to his employees. He decided to follow conventional wisdom by breaking the news on the day the deal was complete.

Alex counted the days until closing. The guilt was still there, and it still gnawed at him. But while he dreaded telling his employees, he also looked forward to getting it done. It would be like ripping a Band-Aid off or pulling a loose tooth. There was sure to be some pain but getting it over with would be a tremendous relief.

Alex had observed Mekhi and Ron with interest after they signed the stay agreements—especially Ron. Both men fulfilled their end of the bargain to keep quiet and comport themselves professionally. Mekhi remained extremely busy keeping up with managed services, and there was little difference in his updates during meetings. But Ron's presence changed radically.

A&S's longtime project manager had asked far fewer questions and raised no objections over the last six leadership meetings. He provided sufficient and straightforward updates on current projects before handing the floor to the next team member. Alex thought he could detect a certain smugness but had to admit the perception might be in his head—he was still a little bothered by the project manager's hardball negotiating tactics. Nevertheless, the change in Ron's behavior was so unusual that Alex almost feared it would tip people off to the sale.

But I think I like him better like this.

Ron's combative nature had sometimes been trying over the years, though it created enough great suggestions and solutions to make him valuable. Still, the project manager's new, no-nonsense approach to doing his job was refreshing. Alex occasionally smiled, shook his head, and wondered how long it would continue once he reported to Frank.

He'll probably do fine, and it won't be my problem anyway. Probably.

Alex's transitional role in the new company was still unclear. Frank remained vague about the position beyond giving him a list of post-closing action items. Alex started to get the feeling that his responsibilities would be less than anticipated, and certainly not like running the shop. This bothered him a little since he would have less control over the company's performance. But the possibility was also a relief.

Whatever happened, Alex had to accept it. It wouldn't be his decision once the company changed hands. And it *was* going to change hands.

꙳🐚ᐟ#

July 27th

The days passed slowly as Alex crossed each one off a mental calendar. Finally, the week of closing—scheduled for Friday the 30th—arrived.

Alex was chatting in the break room with Mekhi on Tuesday when he felt his phone buzz. He fished it out of his pocket and read the text from his lawyer:

We need to talk ASAP!! Found a problem in the contract.

Alex's eyes narrowed, and he excused himself with a "Gotta take this." He wondered what would inspire his attorney to text, especially since Larry rarely did it—and *never* asked for anything "ASAP." Alex couldn't even remember the lawyer using an exclamation point. He walked to his office, closed the door, and made the call.

"Hey Alex, I spotted some bullshit," Larry answered abruptly. Swearing was *really* odd.

"Hello to you too, Larry. What's up?"

"I was going over the latest version of the contract and noticed some language I haven't seen before," Larry said. "It seems like they slipped it in a couple of versions ago—I'm sorry for not catching it sooner."

"Ok, what's the ..."

Larry started reciting the passage:

"Any material differences to the assumptions of this agreement based on and after the due diligence period and discovered by the Buyer after closing …"

Alex tried to keep up with the legalese but wasn't wholly successful. He thought he had the gist, however, after hearing the words "reevaluation of As Earned Fees."

"Ok, Larry. Now give it to me in English," Alex said.

"They've basically inserted a screw-you button that they can push at any time and for whatever reason!" Larry said. Alex was taken aback by the lawyer's emotion. He briefly wondered whether Larry was angrier at the new contract, the opposing attorney for pulling a fast one, or himself for not catching it sooner.

"Essentially, if they find any 'material difference' in the numbers or accounts or whatever information they gathered during due diligence, they reserve the right to claw back your backend payouts to compensate for it."

Alex frowned and tried to stay objective as his pulse quickened. "Is that unusual or unfair? Like, what could come back to bite me?"

"It's not unheard of to have some sort of provision like this, but whether it's unfair is unknown," Larry said. "That's the problem. The language is vague enough to cover a lot of things, depending on how you interpret 'material difference.' Does that mean they find some unearned revenue that hasn't been spotted? Or some accounts payable? Or would they try to pull something for simple stuff that's just part of doing business?"

"How much could the hit be on payouts?" Alex asked.

"Essentially, it's TBD on the performance pay based on any

material differences they find. But really, whatever hit they take, you could take. Contracts need to be specific. This is *way* too open-ended."

Alex felt anxiety surging in his chest. He struggled to remain calm and think things through. *Is Frank trying to screw me over?*

"Well, what can we do? What *should* I do?" Alex said.

"Not sign this contract!" Larry said. "As your attorney, I can't recommend you expose yourself to this kind of open-ended risk. It's bullshit."

Alex's heart sank. He thought of all the work to make this deal happen—the concessions he'd already made and the bridges he'd crossed and blown up behind himself. Fear had his full attention now, with panic taking savage stabs at breaking through. Alex took a deep breath, focused, and thought for a moment.

"Can't we just push back?"

"Oh, you bet I'll push back," Larry said. "But closing is only about 36 hours away. That's not a lot of time to get this ironed out. And if they put this in there, I'm not sure how willing they'll be to change it. I can ask them to strike it or cap it. If they don't, I have to advise you not to sign. I know that's a hard pill to swallow at this point, but I think it would ultimately be in your best interest."

"One thing at a time," Alex said irritably. "Contact their attorney ASAP and ask for as much clarity on this as possible. Push back and see if they'll budge. Let me know immediately what they say. If they won't compromise, I'll give Frank a call and see what we can do. Now, let's move."

"Ok, I'm on it. I'll let you know ASAP," Larry said and hung up.

Alex put the phone down and his head in his hands.

Jesus. Why the hell can't this just go easy? What is Frank trying to pull? Calm down. Focus. The deal isn't dead yet, and maybe Larry is overreacting.

Alex once again considered whether the attorney's anger affected his legal judgment—if he was *more* focused on getting played and missing something than what was right for Alex. He decided that those might be factors, but the attorney was genuinely worried about how this might play out. The only problem with Larry's analysis was that it was limited to the legal and financial implications. He probably didn't fully grasp Alex's emotional investment in selling or how preparing for a sale but aborting it would impact the business if the deal fell through.

Could he really stay engaged in running the business? How would Ron and Mekhi react if it didn't happen? Ron was set for a big payday and Mekhi a pretty good one—could Alex even keep them happy and on the team? Then, there was the thought of being free. If he refused to sign, he'd be back where he was a few months ago, only *more* tired.

If Alex wanted to sell again, he might not get the number he had now or have to sell to someone who would take the clients and fire the employees. Regardless, he'd have to go through this entire painful process all over again.

Alex pushed the panic down deep.

Chill out. Breathe. One thing at a time. Let's see what the lawyers come back with—and then I need some advice.

Alex called Kristi while he waited for the lawyers. His wife offered emotional support but didn't have the answers he craved. The conversation calmed him down, though, which was a good thing. Alex had snapped at Kevin when the salesman knocked on his door and entered during the call. And freaking out his employees was the last thing Alex needed. He had just finished his apology to Kevin when Larry called.

"They said they'll talk to Frank, but it seems like no dice," Larry said.

Alex decided to take the bull by the horns and call Frank himself.

"Frank, we've got an issue with the contract."

"Yes, I've heard. What are your concerns?"

"First, why did you guys insert this 'material differences' bit into the contract? What are you worried about?" said Alex.

"Well, it was the lawyers who suggested it, just as an emergency provision," Larry answered.

Uh-huh. Put it on the lawyers.

"Essentially, it's just one of those things that I'm sure we'll never need," Frank said. "But look: I've done a couple of deals and gotten seriously burned. After one acquisition, we found some unearned revenue the company had booked wrong, and there was nothing I could do. So, I wound up on the hook for almost $200,000! And it was a mistake I swore I'd never make again."

"So, if I were you, I'd just ask yourself: 'Is there a possibility I have anything big like that out there?'" Frank continued. "If you don't, then there is nothing to worry about. That's the only type of scenario where that would come into play."

"I don't think so, and I understand your concerns," Alex said. "But I also think that's the problem with the language. It's a little vague on what counts as a 'material difference.'"

"Understood. But that's because we don't know what we don't know," Frank said. "But I *do* know this: Cam is one of the best financial auditors in the business, and I believe he found everything big that will make a difference. This is just something that helps me sleep at night and shares the risk between us."

"Also, I hope you understand I have zero intention of screwing you over or somehow giving you a bad deal," Frank continued. "Not in the least! We've known each other for about 10 years, and people know you in this industry. I wouldn't get where I am by doing that. Further, I like you, and I'll need your help bringing A&S into the fold. You have my word that we'll be fair and that this is just a safety measure."

Alex thanked Frank for his perspective and said he'd discuss it with his lawyer. While Frank said he might be open to slight changes, he stood firm that the clause would remain. Alex put the phone down and stared at his closed office door. Frank's response seemed sincere, though the man had also tried to deflect responsibility to his lawyer before explaining the real reason: winding up on the hook for a couple hundred thousand dollars of unearned revenue in another deal. And sincerity and trust only went so far in business.

Alex picked up the phone again and texted his old mentor, Jason. Twenty minutes later, the phone rang, and Alex explained the situation.

"Well, what do you think?"

"It's a tough one. I get your concerns, and I get his. I've gotten a few nasty surprises after the ink was dry," Jason said. "And it doesn't sound like he's open to striking that part of the deal. So, essentially, you've got to answer a few questions to decide what to do."

"One: How thorough was the due diligence, and did you guys miss anything relevant?"

"Two: If something comes out of the backend, can you live with it? Or could you live with killing the deal and staying on or trying to sell again?"

"And three: Trusting anyone completely in business is a bad idea. But you do know this guy; is it in his best interests or nature to try and screw you over?"

"An accountant can probably help you with question number one," Jason continued. "But only *you* know the answers to the other two. And, unfortunately, that last one is a combination of good judgment *and* a leap of faith."

"It sure is," Alex said. "Thank you, Jason. You've been a massive help during this whole process. I really regret falling out of touch. Man, I should have at least hired you as a consultant—or maybe a therapist—a long time ago."

"No problem, buddy," Jason said with a laugh. "Happy to help. Oh, one other suggestion that's a little more specific. He doesn't want to remove or significantly change that part of the contract. But if you're worried about it being vague and getting screwed somehow, maybe suggest some sort of arbitration clause. Like, if the material differences exceed a certain amount and you contest it, you have the automatic right to enter into mediation or arbitration with a neutral third party."

"That's a possible course anyway if you decided to contest something and pursue legal remedies but putting it in writing is a shot across their bow not to try anything funny. Plus, it's a naturally fair thing to add—mediation is impartial, and so is arbitration, though the decision is out of both of your hands in the latter case. So, I think it will be harder for them to turn down that mild change."

"That's not a bad idea," Alex said. He again marveled at how helpful Jason had been.

"Good luck, man, and go do some fast thinking," Jason said. "In the end, I'm sure you will make the best decision for you. Let me know what happens."

꧁☙꧂#

Alex forwarded the arbitration suggestion to his lawyer and told him to broach the change. Then he drove to the corner coffee shop to relax and think.

Alex reviewed the due diligence and couldn't see any hidden holes. He thought of the business and his legacy. Alex considered his options: pulling the plug on the deal or finding another buyer. At this point, running the business for another few years wasn't a realistic option. In his heart, he knew what he was going to do. What it seemed like he had to do.

He was going to sign the contract.

Coming Clean,
Part 2

Aㅤ LEX TOOK A DEEP BREATH as he stood in the hallway outside the conference room. Closing was tomorrow, but he'd
decided to tell the leadership team a day earlier than the rest of the
employees. He owed them that, at least.

Alex walked into the room, greeted everyone, and sat down at
the head of the table. The team was quiet and curious. They knew
something was up—this was not a regularly scheduled meeting,
and none of his people were stupid. Alex wondered how much they
knew or suspected; whether Ron or Mekhi had dropped any hints or
if his own behavior had tipped them off. The energy in the office had
seemed a little different over the past week. None of it mattered now.

"I'm sure you all are wondering why I called a leadership meeting on a Thursday," Alex said. "I have a big announcement to make,

and I want you all to know before I tell the rest of the team. I am selling A&S."

He briefly looked at each team member. All of them were attentive and silent, but he caught Kevin's wide eyes and saw Dani put her hand to her cheek. Ron was relaxed—too relaxed. If the feisty project manager failed to ask any probing questions, everyone would certainly figure out that he already knew.

"I realize this comes as a surprise, maybe even a shock. But before we get into it, I want you to understand that this does not mean everything will change," Alex said. "I'm selling to a guy who runs another MSP near Princeton who wants to expand into our area. He thinks we have a quality team and a great business, so he wants to keep it intact. For the most part, things should keep running just like they do—and I'll be around for a while to make sure the transition goes smoothly."

"Wow," Ron said, leaning forward in his seat. "When is this happening?"

"The contract will be finalized tomorrow," Alex said. "I wanted to tell everyone earlier, but it wasn't realistic to do it during the sales process." Alex chided himself for making excuses—it was a little weak and probably sounded hollow anyway. But he couldn't help himself.

"Like I said, A&S will continue—things should not change drastically just because it's being sold," he continued quickly. "A huge reason I chose this buyer was because he recognized our success and wants that to continue. We'll have a meet and greet with the new owner and some of his team on Monday, and you will all have some action items to help with the transition."

"So … you are saying that all of our jobs are safe?" Dani asked cautiously.

"Ye—they should be," Alex said, chiding himself again. "Let me shoot you as straight as possible: you all still have jobs as of now. Again, Frank, who will be your new boss, bought this company because it works, and he does not want to mess with success. But you will all have to meet with him individually to discuss your roles and, of course, he will own the business—so he will make final decisions. But I believe this may open up more opportunities for many of you, as he runs a bigger MSP that is now becoming an even bigger one. And I think he wants to expand further."

Dani nodded, sat back in her chair, and looked at the table. Alex wasn't sure he'd played that perfectly. But he couldn't think of any other way to handle it without making promises he couldn't keep.

"So, you don't *know* if he's going to make some changes," Ron said coolly.

He can't help himself, thought Alex with grim amusement. *At least it's true to form.*

"Well, I won't own the business, so I can't sit here and make blanket promises about anything," Alex said. "But I *can* tell you that—again—he wants to keep A&S doing what it's doing. Some interested buyers wanted our client list and to cherry-pick employees, but Frank really wanted *A&S.* You guys know the clients, systems, projects, and how everything else works. I don't imagine he's going to mess with that much. And I will still be here for a while."

Mekhi sat attentively. Ron had leaned back in his chair with his arms crossed. Dani looked pensive, as did Kevin—both of them probably knew that account management and sales were not totally immune to redundancy. Acacia was characteristically unreadable.

"Why are you selling?" Kevin asked.

"I've been running A&S for almost 20 years, and I just think it's time," Alex said. "Honestly, I'd like a break and maybe to try something new. And certainly spend a little more time with my kids before they are out of the house. The company is doing well financially, and we have a great client list, so don't worry about that. That's what makes it a good time to sell. I'm sure you guys have a lot more questions. I'm happy to answer them now—we've got the rest of the hour—and individually afterward."

"Do you know if—"

Dani's question was cut short by the sound of Acacia's chair dragging against the carpet.

"Excuse me." Her voice was strange. The bookkeeper quickly stood up and left the conference room, closing the door firmly behind her.

Everyone stared at her and then at Alex. Alex's brows knitted together, and his mouth was open.

What was that? Oh my God. She's upset. What do I do?

Alex quickly recovered and resisted the urge to run out the door after her.

"Guys, I want you all to know a few things. I value this team immensely, and it's an honor to work with all of you," he said. "When I decided to sell, I made it a priority to find a buyer who recognized how good you are and what we've accomplished. Again, I can't sit here and make guarantees once I've handed over the keys—I can't promise Frank won't change *anything*. But you have all proven your value, he knows your ROI, and I've communicated that to him strongly. And I will still be around for a bit and have your back after the sale."

"I believe this is a good thing for A&S and the team," Alex continued. "It will be a bigger company with more resources and more opportunities to grow. I know each of you will perform well—and you will always have my support. It really has been an honor. Thank you."

Dani, Kevin, and Mekhi thanked Alex in return, while Jason nodded before leaning forward to speak. The look on his face signaled a question was coming.

"For now, let's table the questions until I meet with each of you individually today. One very important thing: I've let you know a little early—I'm making the general announcement tomorrow. Please don't tell anyone else until I have the chance to do it."

He looked at everyone briefly to make sure they agreed before walking quickly out of the conference room. Alex rushed to Acacia's office.

❧ 🐚 ⚑ #

Alex knocked on the closed door. No answer and no sounds. He gently knocked again.

"Acacia, it's Alex," he said. "Do you have a few minutes to talk?"

"Just a minute," she replied softly. "Come in."

Alex opened the door, and his heart sank. Acacia had obviously been crying. A tissue and her phone were on the desk in front of her. His head spun.

Acacia was a rock—a pillar of strength. Alex had anticipated some surprise and maybe a little anger, but getting upset? There was also something else in her eyes: fear.

"Acacia: are you ok? Talk to me," Alex said.

"No, not really," she answered bitterly. "I'm sorry. This is *not* a good time to lose my job. And I'm beyond shocked that you are dropping this on us without notice." *There* was the anger.

"Acacia, just because A&S is being sold doesn't mean you are going to lose your—"

"Oh c'mon, Alex," she cut him off. "You and I both know that the numbers people are always the first to go. Your buyer has his own person who does the books, and they have their own systems. So yeah, they'll keep me on for a few weeks; maybe even a couple of months during the transition. And then they'll have zero need for my position."

She stared accusingly. Her eyes were still wet but now cold. Acacia may have cried alone in her office, but she sure as hell wasn't going to do it in front of him. Alex felt sick to his stomach. He knew she was probably right.

"Listen: I will do everything I can to keep you on," he said softly. "And if they do let you go, I will help you find another position and a soft landing. You are very good at what you do. You've been my rock in this business, and plenty of companies would be lucky to have you. We'll—"

"I am a 48-year-old bookkeeper!" she blurted out. Fear and sadness had switched places with anger. "People just aren't lining up to hire someone like me. Most of them have their own people. And if they do, they certainly aren't going to give me the pay or benefits I have here. I have a mortgage, two kids in college, and a husband who can't work anymore. And I'm going to lose our health insurance. *What am I going to do?*"

"How is David? I thought he was doing better?" Alex said.

Though she'd worked for him for almost a decade, Acacia tended to keep her private life separate from work. Alex knew that she had two children and a husband who had multiple sclerosis. But she rarely talked about them unless asked, and Alex had never met them.

"His MS is progressive, and he's having some new issues," she said. "The drugs he was on aren't working that well anymore. He is often in pain, and he can barely walk. We're exploring some new options, and I may need to hire a home health aide. No idea how I'll be able to pay for that now." Acacia put her head in her hands.

Alex's stomach dropped. My lord. I've been tied in knots for months over selling the business, but those aren't real problems. These are.

"I am so sorry, Acacia, I had no idea," he said. "Listen … please look at me. I will help you. I will do whatever I can to make sure you land on your feet. I may be leaving A&S, but I'm not exactly out of the industry. I will work my contacts to help you get a good position—*if* it's necessary. Please believe that. I understand why you're worried, and there's a lot of uncertainty. But we will figure this out."

She looked up at him. The worry was still written on her face, but he thought he saw some relief. Though, it might just be resignation.

"Thank you, Alex," she said without much warmth. "I appreciate the thought, and I apologize for leaving the meeting. This is just a shock at a very bad time. But I'm sorry … I just still don't understand why there was no notice this was happening. After about a decade of working for you, I would have liked to know."

Alex winced. He considered saying why it was a bad idea to tell employees about a sale. He could explain that decision in terms of "best practices" and how it might kill a sale or lower the price. That employees might leave or cut back on their work. That telling people only caused more uncertainty and worry and doing so could damage a business long term if the deal never happened. But none of those things would matter to her, and Alex's problems seemed hollow in comparison.

"I just … I didn't think it was a good idea," he said. "I'm sorry that I couldn't tell you sooner."

"Ok. Thank you for talking with me," Acacia said in an even tone that signaled an end to her vulnerability. "I've got a couple of calls to make, and I have to finish the monthly reports, so I'd better get back into it."

"Alright. I'll leave you to it," Alex said. "But please remember: we *will* figure all this out. I have your back."

"Thank you."

Alex left awkwardly and shut her door behind him. He walked down the hall toward his office.

Financial schedules. Stay agreements. Unearned revenue. Backend payments and money up front. MMR. Top-line revenue and contracts. These details had dominated his life for months, along with the anxiety that was part of obsessing over them. But he was now reminded—and the recurring guilt meant he'd *always* known—that a business was far more than the sum of these numbers, processes, and objectives. It's a living entity comprised of human beings.

Selling the business wasn't just a decision about what he was doing with his life. He was deciding the course of dozens of other people's lives, too. And there was simply no way around some of them getting hurt.

Alex looked up and saw Kevin waiting outside his office. He straightened up, walked forward, and motioned the sales manager into it.

Celebration
and Sentiment

July 30th

ALEX SAT AT A LONG wooden table in the law firm's conference room. Kristi was to his left, Frank and his attorney were
across the table, and several tall stacks of paper sat before him. A
bottle of champagne chilled in the corner of the room. Larry walked
in and grabbed the chair to Alex's immediate right. The lawyer had
made peace with the contract and his client's wishes, and he was now
all business.

"Ok, everyone ready?" Larry said.

"Let's do this," Alex said as Frank nodded.

Larry took the lead, placing each page in front of the signers
and explaining what they were endorsing under the other attorney's
watchful eye. Alex listened carefully as the lawyer broke each condition down in plain English, though he started to lose focus by the

twentieth signature or so. Each party had to sign two copies apiece of about 250 pages. The closest thing Alex had experienced to this was signing a mortgage, but that took a fraction of the effort. The process almost seemed ludicrous.

When they reached the claw-back provision over any "material difference" after the sale—now with an arbitration clause—Alex looked at Larry. To the lawyer's credit, he buried any signs of disapproval.

They hit the final page of the agreement about an hour later. Alex and Frank signed their copies with sore hands, stood up, and met at the head of the table.

"Congratulations, Alex," Frank said, shaking Alex's hand vigorously.

"Congratulations to you, too. You've bought a great company. Now, take care of it," Alex said.

"You bet I will. Now, it's time for a drink."

Alex hugged Kristi while Frank walked over to the ice bucket and expertly worked the cork free from the champagne bottle. He poured five glasses and handed them out.

"A toast to A&S and a bright future for both of us," Frank said.

"Here, here," said Alex.

"The money has been transferred," Frank's attorney chimed in. "Just in case you need something more to celebrate."

Alex smiled broadly. Relief flooded his body—even joy. There was still so much to do: make the announcement to the entire team, start working on the transition, and reorient his life to no longer running a business. But he felt like a massive weight had been lifted off his back.

Selling A&S had been far more challenging than he'd thought it would be. The process had been surprising, stressful, and often disappointing, but now it was done. And while the business had sold for less money than Alex had hoped—and there were still questions about how much he'd eventually receive—it was still a lot of money. Even the $400,000 just wired to his bank account was more than 99 percent of people would ever get paid at once. Alex knew that he wasn't necessarily set for life. But he was consciously grateful for what he'd achieved and the *opportunity* it presented.

Alex had the freedom to make a new life. The future was wide open. And whether that future involved spending more time with his kids, pursuing a passion project, or even starting a new business, he would be doing it because he *genuinely wanted to do it*. Running A&S had been his passion for many years, but that enthusiasm always mixed with intense pressure. In the early days, it was the need to survive and provide for his family. Later, it became the stress of growing the business and being responsible for so many employees. Now, Alex felt that he would be playing with house money—he could at least afford to be happy about whatever he chose to do.

No, he didn't have the resources never to work another day in his life. But he certainly had enough that whatever he decided to do wouldn't be an existential struggle. He knew that most people only dreamed about such freedom.

Alex consciously savored the moment as he finished his glass of champagne and chatted with Frank, Kristi, and the attorneys. Eventually, he checked his watch.

It was time to head back into the office and close this deal with the last difficult task. But while telling the rest of the employees would be tough, Alex had lost much of the guilt and discomfort that had gripped him for months. The announcement to everyone probably wouldn't be as bad as telling the leadership team. Even if it was, Alex had steeled himself.

These trials and decisions *were business*—and certainly parts of selling one. So, while Alex hadn't become cold, he did begin experiencing some necessary detachment late in the game, aided in no small part by signing the contract. After that pen stroke, it wasn't *his* business anymore. And there was no going back.

Alex would do everything possible to smooth the transition and support his employees. Whatever challenges arose now were inevitable and temporary—and he would deal with them with renewed energy.

꙰ ⍨ ☙ ⌇ #

Aftermath

Alex's general announcement of the sale went easy. He wasn't sure whether the rest of the team was comforted by his assurances or simply knew they could find jobs—almost all of them were IT techs, an in-demand position. Whatever the case, Alex's relief was complete.

That Monday, Frank and several members of his leadership team arrived to conduct an all-hands meeting. Afterward, the office became a busy hive of activity as Frank and his department heads met with key groups to kick off the transition.

Acacia submitted her resignation three weeks after the sale. She'd found an administrative position working for the local school board; Alex suspected it was a pay reduction, but the benefits would be great. He was frustrated that he didn't have the chance to help her find something better but also understood that she wanted certainty. Frank hadn't indicated her job was in immediate danger, but it had still been a good possibility.

Within a month of the sale, the financial systems switched over, and most of the processes were integrated. Frank made fewer appearances in the office as Elise, his right hand, took the reins with the title of managing director. She moved into Acacia's office out of respect for Alex but clearly had eyes on the big chair. And this transition became official—confirming Alex's long-held suspicions—in a conversation with Frank at the end of month two.

Frank thanked Alex for his hard work and praised him for a successful transition. But now that the business was largely integrated and running smoothly, he'd like to move Alex into more of a "consultant role" the following week. Alex saw the writing on the wall and gamely agreed—A&S was doing well, and it made little sense to have more than one boss running around.

Alex worked late on his last Friday in the office, finishing up some action items before clearing out his office. He grabbed an empty paper box and began carefully filling it with personal items: the family pictures, his son's artwork, and the chipped Star Trek mug—no way he was leaving *that* beauty behind. He hesitated at the "Best IT services" award A&S had received 12 years ago after a vote conducted by the local newspaper. Winning the award had taken a lot of lobbying; self-promotion that maybe even resembled begging. It was a small thing in the scheme of an 18-year struggle.

But he vividly remembered the feeling of victory and what it had meant, helping put A&S on the radar of possible clients.

Alex smiled. *Better leave it. That belongs to A&S, not me.*

"Are you going to miss it?"

Alex looked up and saw Mekhi standing in his doorway.

"Oh, hey. Yeah. But maybe not as much as I won't miss the grind," Alex said with a smile. "I'll miss the people, though, that's for sure. What are you doing here this late?"

"I'm about to head out. I was finishing an evaluation of that new client," Mekhi said.

Alex smiled ruefully. One lesson the deal had driven home quickly was that while his backend payouts could be penalized for *losing existing clients* after the sale, he didn't get credit for *new ones.* A week ago, one of A&S's longtime clients downgraded their services, which could impact hitting the performance benchmark for his ideal payment. Meanwhile, A&S had signed a new client. The combined events were an overall plus for the business and a slight setback for Alex.

Nevertheless, the company looked like it would do well, and Alex gained confidence that he'd get the majority of the money. But he also accepted the idea that events may whittle down his payments over three years, at least slightly.

"How are you with everything?" Alex said.

"It's going well. Frank's ok, and Elise really knows what she's doing," Mekhi answered. "I like their ticketing process a little more than ours. They also seem to focus more on MRR and don't accept as many projects, which will keep me busy. How are *you* with everything? Stepping back, I mean."

"I'm good with it," Alex said. "I've done all I can for the transition, and you guys seem like you're on track. Frank is impressed with you, by the way. He says you 'live up to the hype.'" Mekhi grunted, smiled, and looked at the floor.

"Honestly, it's a relief stepping away," Alex continued. "Once you decide to sell a business, you see the light at the end of the tunnel and want to try something new. I'm not sure what that is yet, but I know a nice, long vacation is in my immediate future."

Mekhi smiled broadly now. "I remember those. Well, you've earned it, boss," he said. "It's been an honor working for you, and I've learned a lot. Thank you for everything." They shook hands.

"Same here. I couldn't have done it without you," Alex said, fighting the urge to tear up. "But I'm not *dying*, Mekhi. I'll still be around, you have my number, and you can hit me up for anything. Unless I'm on a beach and I threw my phone in the ocean, maybe. C'mon. I'll walk you out."

They headed toward the front door. Alex looked at the long row of empty cubicles, briefly picturing the busy hub of activity he'd seen on so many days. Mekhi opened the door and held it open.

"It's been a ride, huh?" he said.

"Yeah. A hell of a ride."

Alex keyed the alarm, took a long, last look, shut off the light, and closed and locked the door.

꒰ ꒱ ꒰ #

Alex's phone buzzed on the ride home. It was Jason.

"Hey, Jason."

"Hey, buddy. How's life on easy street?" Jason said.

"I don't know about that, but I'm doing well. What's up with you?"

"Well, I have something I could maybe use your advice on for a change," Jason said. "Several of my clients are asking some operational questions—a lot of them about tech—and I don't have all the answers. IT is not exactly my wheelhouse. But instead of handing them a referral, solving these issues might be a value-add. There could be an opportunity for you here, too. Mind if I pick your brain?"

"Sounds interesting," Alex said. "I like the idea of helping people solve *their* problems, for a change. Fire away."

Nonfictional M&A Case Studies

Rich Anderson
and Next Level Café

Rich Anderson is currently the CEO of Imagine IT, a successful managed services provider with over 40 employees in the Minneapolis–Saint Paul metro area. He's been involved in several business sales and purchases over his career, both directly and as an advisor. In addition to his IT and entrepreneurial experience, Rich has a public accounting background, which was very helpful while conducting due diligence for each transaction. But like many entrepreneurs who have sold or bought businesses, there were plenty of hard lessons he had to learn along the way.

In 2002, Rich bought into his first IT company along with a co-owner, soon renaming it Next Level Café. The company transitioned from a project-based service business into a pure-play managed IT services firm, exclusively focused on monthly recurring revenue (MRM) while providing a few one-off projects for existing clients. The next business he bought was a little different, however.

In 2007, Next Level Café purchased Badbrain Computers, a small firm in nearby Northfield, Minnesota that focused on residential break/fix services along with a bit of retail. The acquisition provided an opportunity to expand revenue, size, and geographic footprint. But while the new venture did ok, Rich and his partner soon ran into problems as they tried to convert it to managed services. Badbrain had good foot traffic and word-of-mouth referrals but targeting businesses to become managed services clients called for an entirely different sales model and attempts at hiring and training local sales staff fell flat.

Within a few years, Rich and his partner decided that greater investment was necessary to penetrate Northfield's managed services market. And ultimately, they'd achieve better ROI by selling the branch and devoting those resources to the main company.

Thus, in 2010, Rich sold a business for the first time. It was a small deal, and both the decision to do it and the transaction went smoothly. Some of this experience proved valuable—but it didn't prepare him for the difficulties of selling the *next* time.

An early mistake sets the stage for struggles. And a break in the partnership imperils the business

In 2010, Next Level Café was doing…ok. The company had a decent stable of loyal clients and generated healthy revenue, but profit margins were slim to none, and the company had sizeable debt.

In retrospect, Rich realized that purchasing the business from his former employer in 2002 was a mistake. They'd obtained the old company's clients, sure. But there was only a handful of them responsible for about 95% of revenue. Within six months of the purchase, three of those clients had left or significantly downsized.

In the end, Rich wound up paying about a quarter of a million dollars—and accruing significant debt—for "something that really didn't have any value."

"That was a time when having some external advice might've been helpful," says Rich. "I basically should have just spun up my own company and started offering the services."

Rich spent the next 10 years "stubbornly trying to prove that it was a good decision," but the financial and operational difficulties created by the purchase were a continuing challenge. The company grew its revenue but struggled to get over the million-dollar mark. Profit margins weren't ideal, and the debt had to be serviced. And in 2010, the departure of a partner would make these problems existential ones.

Rich's partner decided that running the business and living in Minnesota weren't for him anymore. The pair were 50-50 owners but, more significantly, 50-50 *managers*. They divided and conquered whatever needed to be done, and losing his partner's operational investment to silent ownership turned out to be a near-fatal blow. Rich and his team quickly became overwhelmed. Sales, marketing, and operations took serious hits—Next Level Café simply didn't have the leadership bandwidth to get everything done.

Rich started to seriously consider selling the company. But before he could take action, he was called to serve as a juror on a murder trial that lasted for over a month.

"After my partner left, we lost clients, employees, and all sorts of momentum," Rich recalls. "And here I am, going into jury duty every day and watching my company fall apart at the seams. I had to do something, and selling was one way to go."

Soul-searching and assessing options

By 2011, a sense of desperation had set in, and Rich grasped for options. Should he bring on another partner? Take on even more debt and buy out the current one? Declare bankruptcy and walk away? Or try to sell the business outright?

Complicating everything was the company's situation and potential valuation. A core of customers remained with Next Level Café, but it had shed some clients and possessed an incomplete leadership team. It was also in debt to both Rich and the bank. The company's healthy revenue translated to break-even or marginal profits on the balance sheet, at best—and only because Rich took little salary (and sometimes none) while otherwise moving payments around.

"Honestly, we were losing money," he says. "So, how did I communicate that to potential buyers and investors? Pretty honestly, really—the numbers speak for themselves. As I generated financial packets and shared them, you can only put so much lipstick on the pig. It's still a pig, and it looked like one."

Nevertheless, Next Level Café did retain a couple of strong selling points. The company's management team was incomplete, but the rest of the organization, from its services and processes to technicians, worked well. And it had some loyal, recurring-revenue customers. A decade ago, the managed IT services industry was still evolving and maturing. There was a great deal of speculation and experimentation over how to serve customers properly—but the ultimate prize *was the customers*. Fortunately, Next Level Café had nurtured quality clients along with well-designed offerings.

"If you were a buyer with a mature management team, a proven sales process, and a good existing client base that you could cross-sell IT services, then it was a desirable buy," recalls Rich.

After testing the market, Rich was approached with three different proposals:

- An individual wanted to **buy out his partner's share and take the role**, infusing some cash and business acumen.

- A local CPA firm offered to **buy the business outright and keep Rich on to manage it**—as an employee, not a partner.

- The final offer stemmed from a competing MSP who shared a client with Next Level Café. Rich had reached out to them to obtain administrative credentials, followed by a thank-you lunch that evolved into **a merger proposal.**

All three buy offers reflected Next Level's financial situation—the numbers were low. In each case, the money wouldn't necessarily have been enough to resolve the accumulated debt. Further, every proposal was contingent on Next Level Café retaining revenue levels after changing hands. So, there was a very good chance Rich would remain on the hook for a significant amount of money.

"Looking at those three options while keeping the business running and was incredibly challenging, emotional, and confusing," he recalls.

Rich felt depressed and helpless at times, "like a deer in headlights." In other moments, he was angry at his partner for leaving. There were bursts of excitement at the prospect of bringing in someone who could help with leadership, cash flow, and sales. And desperation reared its ugly head: there were points he would've taken anything to pay off the debt and relieve his family from the burden of a failing company.

Whiteboarding a moment of clarity

Rich and his wife Alison, who served as his CFO, struggled to make a decision. Rich recalls that his stress—and the complexity of the choices—got in the way of seeing a path forward.

Finally, they grabbed a whiteboard and mapped out a matrix. The columns reflected each deal plus the options of declaring bankruptcy or hiring someone to run the company while Rich got another job. The rows listed things that were important to him and the family, including:

* Resolving the debt.

* Staying in the entrepreneurial game with some sort of equity stake. Rich did not like working for other companies and still wanted to be an owner.

* Taking care of employees, if at all possible, was vital.

* Similarly, ensuring clients found a good managed-IT-services home was a priority.

One by one, Rich and Alison evaluated the courses of action against the priorities, creating a stack rank for each one. The matrix clarified things immensely—almost miraculously.

"Going into the exercise, I felt trapped. I could not see the path forward," Rich recalls. "But coming out of it, one of the options was obviously the right one; it was ranked number one or two in every single bucket. My wife and I stared at the whiteboard and asked ourselves: why was this not obvious an hour ago?"

The CPA firm's offer was ruled out because the purchase price was trivial and, though he would be kept on, he'd strictly be an employee with zero equity. The potential new partner had some appeal, but the cash infusion might not make enough of a difference, and a potential personality conflict made that marriage a frightening proposition.

Bankruptcy was out—it would have felt like an unacceptable failure—and hiring someone else to manage the company wasn't realistic or attractive.

Merging with a competitor was clearly the best choice. The other company was a good fit for Next Level Café's services, and a merger would enable him to take care of his customers and employees. Rich would also retain some sort of equity stake and gain the other company's resources and support.

Structuring a deal that made sense

Each of the three deals had different possible structures, but all valuations ended up in the same ballpark. And Rich's financial priorities were unchanged. The purchase price had to be tied to him walking out of the deal with a debt-resolution-plan that would resolve the personal and company liabilities while also exiting Rich's existing but silent business partner.

Thus, instead of using a profit and loss-based valuation to inform the price, the merger called for more of a balance-sheet valuation. Next Level Café had some cash and accounts receivable that it would hold onto while the merged company would take on the debt. There was very little money that would change hands.

The two parties essentially created a large loan that was serviced over three years. Paying off the loan resolved the old debt, plus generated some profit. In the end, Rich and his new partners didn't use traditional enterprise value multipliers like EBITDA or revenue. The number was determined by what was needed to accomplish things Rich could live with, and the purchaser was willing to pay (on a schedule they were all ready to pay it).

In addition to taking care of the debt, Rich's former partner was bought out (mostly by resolving his portion of the debt), and Rich became a one-third owner of the new company and its CEO.

The deal had achieved his goals: getting out of debt and avoiding bankruptcy, obtaining equity, and taking care of clients and employees. But those weren't the only benefits.

Relief and excitement in a post-merger culture

The companies fit together so well that the deal itself, aided by a merger and acquisition firm, went very smoothly. The firm put together the purchase agreement, the shareholder's agreement, and more than a dozen other elements of the document set. The parties' attorneys reviewed the documents, everyone signed and initialed, and the deal was done. Unlike many transactions of this nature, there were no material issues that called for last-minute changes.

Rich felt a massive wave of relief. He had a fresh start.

"Long before the sale, my wife and I and had created a debt-paydown schedule on this big, fancy Excel spreadsheet," Rich recalls. "Regardless of the different scenarios we'd run, paying everything off would have taken years and years."

The sale relieved the family of that burden and enabled Alison to stop working for the company. This, in turn, allowed the couple to stop letting stressful business conversations bleed into their family life.

"We celebrated this transaction because of the financial relief. But it also allowed us to reboot our personal life," says Rich. "That was huge. It was awesome."

He hadn't just improved his personal life and dodged a financial bullet, however—Rich also entered into something new and exciting. While the deal was an acquisition—Next Level Café *was* being gobbled up by a competitor—the organizations and their leaders culturally treated it like a merger. The two companies fit together well: their technology stacks, support structures, services, and pricing models were very similar, and there would be little delay in each entity ramping up to service the other's clients.

More importantly, Rich was no longer alone. The merger meant that he'd finally have the support his previous company had needed for some time, including great sales, ops, relationship, and financial managers.

"The team I'd never had was finally sitting in front of me," Rich says. "In previous years, some of my colleagues in a peer group had quadrupled in size while we had stayed the same. There are a lot of variables to that. But, looking back, the most telling one was having the right people on their team."

"Without any support, I had been the bottleneck," he continues. "After the deal, I was very excited about the possibility of achieving a lot of the things that I knew I was capable of but didn't have the resources to do."

When the companies merged, each was doing roughly a million dollars in revenue. A year later, the new venture hit the three-million-dollar mark.

Lessons learned and mistakes made

Rich's deal is a business-sale story with a happy ending. But looking back, he recognizes numerous mistakes and things he could have done better.

The biggest one, he notes ruefully, is buying Next Level Café in the first place instead of building his own firm. It set the stage for most of the critical challenges that followed, including the debt that forced a deal and impacted the company's valuation.

Another error was entertaining potential offers that he knew he'd never take. He believes it's a mistake to consider options for longer than their useful life.

"I had some offers that I knew were probably not what I was interested in. But I told myself it would be a good learning experience to go through the process of determining the sale price," Rich explains. "The reality is that I knew the offers were going to be low, and I didn't want to work with those people. I should've aborted faster. Every ounce of energy you put into that is energy you're not putting elsewhere, like finding a better option, upselling clients, or working with employees."

Finally, while Rich feels fortunate the merger took care of his employees and clients, he believes he worried too much about these issues.

"In hindsight, it was probably more ego than anything," he explains. "I think my employees were all highly capable and would have proven themselves worthy to any acquiring company—or they would've gotten another job elsewhere. And my clients would have found a new provider and probably been taken care of just fine. But I think there was some ego involved—me wanting to see the thing I had built live on."

Almost a decade after the sale, Next Level Café *is* Imagine IT, where Rich still serves as CEO and has the same partners. The old debt is long gone, the company is profitable, and it continues to grow.

Advice to other business owners and sellers

As for what Rich thinks other entrepreneurs should consider when selling a business or entertaining a sale, his advice ranges from very practical to philosophical.

First, he discovered that some accounting wrinkles could cause issues during a merger. For example, how one company recognizes billing and revenue—and at what timing—can cause blind spots and periods of missing revenue. Merging companies *must* synchronize their revenue recognition. Similarly, both business buyers and sellers should pay close attention to a company's unearned revenue, as it may inflate the perceived value when those services haven't been delivered yet.

"It's essential to have professionals conduct this due diligence and ask those types of questions," he says. "So you understand what you're getting into, and you make sure you have the cash reserves after the transaction to deal with them."

In addition, Rich recommends never falling in love with a single type of transaction if there are multiple realistic options.

"A seller can become blind to the other possibilities," he says. "You are also not the buyer, and they have their own way of doing things. So, whether you *really* want more cash up front, or you are set on an equity or venture capital sale, step back a little. Remain open and willing to discuss various things."

Another fundamental piece of advice is building a solid team to aid in the due diligence and sales processes—including the legal, financial, human resources, and cultural aspects of the business.

"It doesn't need to be an existing management team. It might be friends of yours or peer group members," he says. "But you need a strong group that can keep you honest and help you focus on the right path forward. Have your team ready to go way before the transaction happens, so they are ready to go at game time."

Rich's biggest takeaway from the experience is more fundamental. And it genuinely applies to how you run a business—and live your life—*long before* you sell it.

"This merger has a happy ending, but my life now makes me realize how things really were before the deal," Rich says. "I didn't realize how much I was struggling and needed a supporting management team. And how many sacrifices we made as a family."

His current company is vastly different and shows how the previous one should have operated. In the end, these differences impact both the valuation of any company and the quality of life enjoyed by its owners.

"Almost a decade after the merger, we continue to enjoy being partners, growing our company, engaging in healthy conflict, and coming up with new sales strategies and offerings. And as CEO, I'm responsible for strategy and visionary thinking, rather than being buried in and overwhelmed by operations," Rich explains.

"I'm in my happy place, and so are the other owners. And I am extremely thankful and blessed to be where I'm at today."

Dave Sobel
and Evolve Technologies

I f you'd asked a young Dave Sobel what he wanted to do for a living a few decades ago, he'd have told you, "I want to be in computers." He certainly achieved that goal, obtaining a computer science degree, running an IT managed services provider (MSP), and working for tech companies, big and small, in various positions. Today, Dave's a media entrepreneur who *talks about* "computers." He owns MSP Radio, which hosts the *Business of Tech* and *Killing IT* podcasts.

Dave has also been involved in two business sales during his career while sitting on either side of the table. One deal that involved buying a competitor was "a spectacular failure." Fortunately, these lessons were valuable—when Dave decided to sell his business several years later, he took the "complete opposite approach."

Imbued with what Dave describes as a "healthy realism," the sale was a success that enabled him to move on to a new stage of his career.

Early IT jobs lead to an entrepreneurial epiphany

Dave started out in technology in the early '90s, doing consulting and software development during the Internet boom. There was a lot of opportunity, though many of these startups eventually crashed and burned. When they did, Dave observed that the people who made the technology—or made it work—were often the first to lose their jobs, while executives escaped the failures with golden parachutes. Eventually, it struck him that he could "run a company into a wall just as easily as those numbskulls."

So, he launched his first company in 2002: Evolve Technologies was a network infrastructure and services firm that was one of the first real "managed services providers." While most of the industry was still using a "break-fix" model—clients only paid when they had problems—Dave saw the value of monthly recurring revenue early.

"I recognized that the flaw for me in services would be chasing refilling the coffers every month," he says. "You'd have to sell continually, and I didn't want to play that game."

Evolve was positioned as an outsourced IT department for small businesses. There were growing pains as the MSP developed processes and learned how to make services work at a flat rate, but the firm soon found its footing and grew organically.

Five years after starting his company, Dave was approached by the owner of another local managed services outfit who was looking to sell. This competitor was smaller than Evolve Technologies, the owner wanted out, and the acquisition looked like an excellent opportunity to accelerate growth.

Deal #1: "A spectacular failure"

Looking back, Dave doesn't have many good things to say about the buy.

"I screwed up so much of that deal," he says. "It taught me a lot, but I cannot say anything about it was successful. The one thing I got right was that the deal structure was built correctly, because it protected me from all the fallout."

The agreement was essentially an "asset purchase:" Evolve merely bought the MSP's existing contracts and hired its employees. On the plus side, the deal was largely execution-based—roughly 4/5 of the payout was tied to performance and the retention of clients over time.

Unfortunately, this execution went poorly. Dave did not anticipate how integrating the clients and new employees would disrupt his existing business. And in retrospect, his due diligence was terrible:

- The client contracts looked good on the surface, but they were pure month-to-month agreements, which drastically reduced their value.

- Dave underestimated the effort needed to integrate new clients and employees on day one. Applying his existing company's methodology causes chaos and impacted service across the board.

- Trying to introduce disciplined processes to both new clients and employees fell flat. Evolve lost most of these accounts and workers quickly.

"The moment I tried to impose my process of discipline on those new customers and hires, things started to disintegrate," Dave says.

One employee who refused to sign an employment contract went so far as to leave and take a big client with him. Dave was stunned and conflicted. On the one hand, he had shown the team member a great deal of trust, and he still viewed that as a positive move. On the other, that trust was mixed with overconfidence—and it had come back to haunt him.

Lessons learned

In retrospect, Dave realizes that he should have heeded numerous warning signs before the buy. First, he wasn't allowed to dig into the other company's full financials. He also wasn't permitted to interview employees or customers. The seller refused because they retained a software development aspect of the business and "didn't want to spook people." They also reasoned that it wasn't a full sale, simply a purchase of assets.

"I did not correctly identify a bunch of things that are, in hindsight, obvious red flags," says Dave.

The failure to get to know employees resulted in a cultural mismatch and most of them were gone within six months of the sale. Dave learned lessons about the importance of documenting efforts to improve employee performance before letting individuals go.

The experience was stressful, and Dave's biggest frustration was that the acquisition impacted the service provided by his core company. Fortunately, Evolve Technologies retained its existing clients. And after untangling itself from the failed purchase, his business again grew organically.

The decision to sell

Evolve Technologies experienced several years of growth and stability, but the company encountered fresh challenges in Dave's last year as owner. For starters, they'd taken on a huge, difficult client. Dave struck the agreement knowing that it demanded significant resources, so this wasn't a surprise. What was a shock, however, was the simultaneous departure of two key employees. Dave faced a challenging situation and, ultimately, a choice about what he wanted to do with his life.

Finding, hiring, and training two new senior managers would involve a great deal of work and time, as would servicing the new client. And as Dave reflected on the effort and the ups and downs of running the company for the past 10 years, he wasn't sure if he wanted to make the commitment.

"I was 36 at the time. I was coming up on my 10th anniversary with my wife, which was also about how long I'd run the business. I took a close look at how I was spending my energy and time—that non-renewable asset," Dave explains. "I knew that if I re-committed to the business, I'd probably be doing it for another five to 10 years. And I just asked myself: is this what I want to be doing in another decade?"

His answer was "no." Dave loves technology and always had a passion for learning. He decided that he wouldn't be learning new things or developing different aspects of his career. Dave wanted fresh challenges.

Fortunately, he experienced an epiphany while looking for solutions to the business's latest challenges.

"I was analyzing the assets and had a moment of inspiration: *there is value here*. In a way, the only lack of value is *me*: I'm unwilling to be the leader this company requires. But Evolve had great recurring revenue and great employees. And those assets—minus the leadership piece—are what a lot of acquiring companies want."

Deal #2: Full disclosure leads to a successful sale

Once he'd decided to explore a sale, Dave's friendly relationships with local competitors paid off.

"I simply called up a few of them. One had an almost annual tradition: we'd do dinner or lunch, and they'd say, 'Whenever you want to sell Dave, let us know.' So, I called them up and said, 'Hey, this is the year I'm interested in having that conversation.'"

Dave had several potential buyers, but one thing he didn't have was a good grip on the company's valuation. He had a loose idea of methods like industry multiples of Earnings Before Interest, Taxes, Depreciation, and Amortization (EBITDA). Still, He recognized that numerous factors determine the price—and a business is only worth what someone is willing to pay for it. Dave eventually reached out to his network and found some merger and acquisition experts who provided valuable consulting.

He also applied the lessons learned from his past purchase, taking "the exact opposite" approach.

"After I'd been talking with one group and we'd signed an NDA (non-disclosure agreement), I said, 'I'm going full open kimono,'" Dave recalls. "Anything you want to know; I will answer that question. You're going to have access to my books; you can obviously review my contracts. And if you need to talk to people, we'll find a reason to do it. 'We will figure this out together' was my attitude."

The eventual deal involved "a very fair and balanced approach:"

* Dave's payment was roughly 25% up front and 75% over two years. He remained available to help and answer questions but did not stay on in a management role.

* The backend payout was conservative and "almost expected things not to go very well." It was based on a percentage of retained revenue that minimized risk but provided the opportunity to exceed expectations and achieve a total payout early.

* The acquiring company had the leadership team to replace the personnel Evolve suddenly lost, so key employee contracts weren't part of the deal. But Dave stipulated that the buyer had to make job offers to his existing employees and give them a fair shot.

The entire deal was characterized by transparency, collaboration, and trust, which were helped by Dave's years of networking and relationship with the buyer. The buyer even pointed out that his initial valuation seemed a "little low."

"They had some opportunities to 'take advantage' of me or something like that, but they never did," he says. "So, you realize these are good people. And they will take care of my people after I'm gone."

The sale and subsequent integration of the companies went smoothly. The processes, people, clients, and financials were a good fit, and retained revenue exceeded their conservative expectations. The purchasing company wound up keeping about 85% of its new revenue over the next three years, Dave received the full backend payout early, and every Evolve employee who wanted a job kept one.

Aftermath: lessons learned and the freedom to take on new challenges

After signing on the dotted line and later completing a successful trial period, Dave was content with the sale—and more than a little excited.

"It was very much a relief when it was concluded, and there was satisfaction that we did a good deal. But the overwhelming feeling was, 'Wow. I've done it. The business is no longer mine, and I have the freedom to do the next adventure.'"

Dave embarked on a third phase of his career that allowed him to "learn new things." In the next eight years, he worked in management positions for a software vendor and various versions of an IT Service Management (ITSM) solutions provider. He helped build two companies that were later snapped up by industry giants and experienced being part of a major initial public offering (IPO). Now, he's an entrepreneur again, running a media company focused on technology and the IT industry.

"Until the day I retire, I will be very, very happy that I sold my company when I did. It was a foundation to build all of the next chapters."

Dave's experience buying and selling businesses gives him a unique perspective that may apply to other entrepreneurs looking to exit. Being burned by insufficient due diligence during a purchase caused him to prize openness and collaboration when it came time to sell.

"I don't think there's a ton of people who sell their business that took the approach I did: 'You can have all of my secrets the moment we start the NDA process," he says. "But [extreme transparency] can apply in a lot of situations, I think. I don't believe in the idea that it's always 'winner takes all' or there are 'only so many pieces of the pie.' The pie can get bigger when people work together. And in a sale, the buyer will find out most of that information anyway if they do the right due diligence."

As for his advice to other potential sellers, his biggest takeaway reflects the ancient Greek aphorism "Know thyself:"

"Know *why* you're selling. You must be honest with yourself on what you're trying to accomplish. Then you can work towards that goal. For me, I knew I was not going to be the person needed to run the business for the next five years, and I wanted to do something else. You need to be clear on the why, and it shouldn't be just to make some money."

Finally, sellers should be pragmatic:

"I've watched people struggle with these deals because they're unrealistic about it," he says. "They think of the effort of building the company and want to make a big pile of money, so they overvalue their business. But nobody buys blood and sweat. Owners who really know *why* they are selling and stay realistic tend to do better."

Arlin Sorensen, HTS, and HTG Peer Groups

Arlin Sorensen's career spans decades as an employee and a business owner, and his entrepreneurial experience includes a combined 10 company acquisitions and sales. He learned many things during these transactions, from the value of due diligence and early preparation to the in-depth communication needed to avoid surprises. But one of the most important lessons is the importance of planning for the aftermath of a sale.

"You want to maximize the value you get out of your company, but there's a lot more to life than money," he says. "You'd better know what you're going to do afterward, or you're going to be miserable."

Fortunately, Arlin figured this out early and threw himself into projects after each sale. These days, he is the VP of Ecosystem Evangelism for ConnectWise, an MSP software provider. Arlin also runs two companies of his own: HTS Ag, which sells precision farming technology, and Oak Road Consulting, which is dedicated to helping small and mid-market businesses grow.

But it all started 36 years ago, back when users accessed the internet with modems, Apple's Macintosh was new, and *Back to the Future* was a hit in theatres.

A small business technology provider grows beyond a "small business"

In 1985, Arlin founded SCCI, an information technology provider focused on delivering products and services to small businesses. SCCI rebranded as Heartland Technology Solutions (HTS) in 2002, and the company eventually settled on a two-pronged strategy that served it well:

- HTS served tertiary white-space markets: the business model was based on having offices within striking distance of major metropolitan areas while not directly competing with firms in those metros.

- From 2000 on, SCCI/HTS grew aggressively by acquiring other companies that were a good fit.

Over about a decade, HTS bought eight companies, expanding its regional footprint and growing to about $17 million in revenue. By 2012, the company had over 100 employees working in seven offices in Iowa, Nebraska, Missouri, Kansas, and Oklahoma.

While the acquisitions and integrations were ultimately successful, each deal presented new challenges.

"There was always one major surprise that I didn't see coming, which frustrated me. Because you'd think after doing eight of them, you'd get it right," Arlin says. "But there was always something you weren't looking for."

Lessons learned on a business-buying spree

The surprises varied from minor but "nagging" issues to ones that wound up having a significant negative financial impact after the purchase. They all had something in common, however: Arlin found that he'd put up with problems once he'd decided to buy a company. And most of them happened after he'd signed a letter of intent (LOI) and right before a deal closed.

"I learned that once you're invested in making a deal happen, you're kind of stuck with whatever you didn't uncover before you got to that point," Arlin says. "So, we learned to do a lot better due diligence earlier and try to uncover as many things as possible. But there was still always a surprise somewhere in the deal."

One of the most frustrating revelations happened during the largest acquisition. Arlin discovered that the company he was buying had presold many services and failed to put it on the balance sheet as a liability—services for which his new, integrated company would be responsible.

"We ended up delivering over a quarter of a million dollars in services without a penny of revenue because customers had the expectation—rightfully so—that they had paid for them," he says.

This liability wasn't spotted until just before the deal was signed, and HTS took a massive hit on the value of the company it was purchasing.

"That was a painful one," Arlin says.

In other buys, he discovered that the sellers had guaranteed key personnel expensive benefits or bonuses. For example, one owner had promised a couple of employees that he would fund their children's college educations. While this was done with the "best of intentions," the owner became distracted by severe health problems and didn't put anything in writing.

"We did not pay the full boat, but we gave them something, and they were appreciative and continued to work for us," Arlin recalls. "But it's always a difficult conversation. You're walking into something where you're not exactly sure what was promised. And you want to want to keep the people, obviously, because they're valuable."

Regardless of due diligence, there were always last-minute issues during the buys. Nevertheless, Arlin tempered his frustration with resolve and resignation.

"Challenges come up, and you just have to make some tough decisions to solve them," he says.

The decision to sell: the right buyer, a passion project, and founder fatigue

Heartland Technology Solutions grew successfully after the acquisitions—too successfully, in one respect. Once the company crested 100 employees, it became subject to a gamut of federal labor and employment laws and reporting requirements. Arlin found the complex rules stifling and decided he "didn't want to live there any longer."

Also, he'd acquired two partners as part of an acquisition in 2003, and they'd always talked about doing a "10-year run." This period was nearing its end by the summer of 2012 when Arlin "got a phone call out of the blue" from a business broker who said they had someone interested in purchasing HTS.

Arlin wasn't necessarily planning to sell his company, but he'd done a lot of planning *for* a sale. First, HTS was always run well, with solid processes and transparent financials that would make it attractive to buyers. Second, after being approached by several potential buyers over the years, Arlin came up with a "non-negotiable list" of conditions that had to be met before he would consider a sale.

The list included 15 items, but the gist was that a purchasing company had to commit to maintaining HTS's business model: serving rural areas around major metropolitan areas. Arlin created this requirement because he wanted to make sure his employees and customers were taken care of. Thus, the non-negotiable list automatically excluded buyers who were just interested in cherry-picking clients and employees while downsizing the company.

"One of the best things I ever did from a seller's perspective was create the non-negotiable list," Arlin says. "The list of items had to be true if we were even going to entertain talking about a sale."

Several interested buyers had been forwarded this list over the years—and all of them had walked away. But the prospect in 2012 agreed to the conditions and pursued an acquisition.

Beyond his concerns about new regulations and finding the right buyer, there were other reasons Arlin decided to sell.

"I was out of gas. Just out of gas," he says. "I was tired of dealing with all of the people and challenges related to running the company."

Arlin also had a side project taking up more and more of his time and energy: building HTG Peer Groups, a professional network for IT professionals.

"That's where my passion was, but the more time that I spent building that, the less time I spent on the computer business," he says. "And it wasn't fair to my partners and team to be halfway in. So, a sale just made sense. The timing was right."

Armed with the right buyer and the motivation to sell, Arlin went after the deal.

A fast, successful sale—but one with a few hard lessons

Arlin had his first meeting with the buyer on October 31, 2012, and, just 60 days later, the deal was complete. This sale was fast and relatively smooth, but it involved new revelations.

First, Arlin discovered what *real* due diligence looked like. The buyer was a large telecommunications company with a board of directors, and they did things thoroughly compared to his previous deals.

"Telcos are very different animals. In November, we had six accountants show up in our office and camp out for a week looking at every piece of paper we had," he recalls. "It all worked out fine, and they were satisfied with what they found. But they uncovered things *we* didn't even know."

And just because the transaction went fast doesn't mean it was easy. On closing day, Arlin wasn't sure it was going to happen.

"The whole process was intense," he says. "It had to close the 31st of December, and by two o'clock on that day, we still didn't have the wire transfer."

Arlin sweated the deal until the money hit the bank account just before 3 pm. And once the sale was complete, aspects of the aftermath were unpleasant. One thing Arlin learned from his acquisitions was the value of keeping his mouth shut about a transaction. Thus, no employees beyond the leadership team had any idea it was happening.

"You don't tell people until it's done because things change, and they change quickly—and at the last minute," he explains. "On my first few deals, I learned that you waste capital by telling everybody. Some deals never happened, and then your team begins to wonder what's really going on and if you know what you're doing."

In addition, revealing details about a big merger or sale creates uncertainty that can harm the organization *and* a transaction.

"The fewer people who know, the better—for sure," Arlin says. "When folks find out, they just put things on pause because they're unsure what the future's going to hold. And you can lose months of productivity while people are second-guessing what's going to happen."

Arlin prioritized the welfare of his employees with the non-negotiable list of sale terms that would help keep the company intact. But employees outside of the executive team *didn't know that*, and he was concerned about how they would react.

HTS sent an executive to each of the seven offices to announce the sale on January 2, and employee reactions varied from quiet acceptance to fear and mourning.

"We actually brought one manager in on the deal the day before it happened," Arlin recalls. "We're sitting in a conference room, and as soon as I said the words 'we are going to sell,' she burst into tears. It turned out that she and her husband had just bought a house. And she was fearful she was going to lose her job, and the sale would jeopardize their plans for the future."

"It was all good after we explained that nothing big would change, and it shouldn't impact her job," he continues. "But it's those kinds of things that make you realize your decisions really impact a lot of people—lots of families and lots of futures. And you've *got to* do things really, really well."

For his part, Arlin felt a mix of emotions after the sale. He was excited because he was very ready to move on. However, Arlin was also frustrated because even though he'd signed a one-year employment agreement to help with the transition, the buyer essentially said he wasn't needed "on day two."

"That caught me off guard," he says. "The way I envisioned the agreement is I would be working side by side and teaching them the ropes, but that was not their intention. It was another assumption, and assumptions are what get you into trouble."

And while the sale succeeded in many respects, it was also disappointing. The deal was structured at 80% cash up front with a 20% earn-out over two years based on top-line revenue. But while the buyer had agreed to Arlin's non-negotiable list, they "kind of honored it, but they kind of didn't." The new company wound up downsizing in some markets, and less activity meant less top-line revenue.

"I was naive about the earn-out structure. We did not get 100 percent," Arlin says. "It ticked me off a little—I was disappointed, for sure. It was my first sale, and I wasn't really clear on how we should have protected ourselves better."

Nevertheless, Arlin experienced overwhelming relief after the sale.

"I think one of the things a lot of entrepreneurs deceive themselves about is they don't think they're under much stress," he says. "Within a few days after selling my company, my family said I was a different person."

"There's a lot of stress having a payroll of a hundred people and trying to serve thousands of clients. So, the biggest thing with the sale was that my stress level was lifted in a big way, and I started to enjoy life more than I had in years."

A passion project leads to sale number 2: HTG Peer Groups

Twelve years before the sale and just as Heartland Technology Solutions started chasing growth, Arlin had also founded HTG Peer Groups.

Immediately after the anticipated Y2K crisis, many IT professionals wondered why none of the apocalyptic predictions about computers were happening. So, Arlin called up other industry leaders in Iowa and got three of them to sit down for a meeting. This set the stage for building a professional network throughout the midwestern and western US.

The organization eventually grew from one regional professional group to 20 groups, and Arlin and his colleagues decided it was a business that required more resources. After selling Heartland Technology Solutions, Arlin threw himself into growing HTG

Peer Groups, and the network expanded to 75 regional groups over the next six years.

The passion project paid off, but Arlin and his team realized that they'd hit another wall in resources if they wanted HTG to grow even more. They needed a financial infusion, and selling the company was one way to do it. So, they reached out to some of HTG's sponsor organizations and found a good potential buyer in ConnectWise, where Arlin works now.

Arlin's dominant emotion in this deal was excitement—any worries were eased by HTG's close working relationship with ConnectWise and the size of the opportunity.

"We had 28 people [at HTG Peer Groups] at the time of acquisition. They had over a thousand," he says. "So, they had a lot more resources, but we shared a vision of helping all computer technology business owners succeed. So, it was a great alignment."

Perhaps the only surprise about this deal was the fact that there weren't really any surprises.

"The deal took a lot longer [than the previous sale] because [ConnectWise] was a much bigger company with even more due diligence—continual interaction with their legal and integration team for months. And there were still questions about whether we'd completely get it done," Arlin says. "But the team was just excited because it was a huge opportunity."

Arlin again had a list of non-negotiables, mainly centered around HTG Peer Groups still serving its current markets. And he'd learned his lesson from the last sale, structuring this one as an all-cash deal with no earn-out. There was also a three-year employment agreement that auto-renewed unless he opted out after three years. This time, the contract played out as Arlin anticipated, and he still works at ConnectWise—which has since expanded to over 2,500 employees—today.

The deal was an unqualified success, and Arlin's experience was certainly better than the last one.

"It was different in that I was having fun and just enjoying that ride," he recalls.

Lessons learned and advice to other business owners

Like many entrepreneurs who buy and sell businesses, Arlin acknowledges there was a point where he became so emotionally invested in a deal that he would go through with it, despite unpleasant last-minute surprises. But he firmly believes that creating a list of non-negotiables well before a sale limited those negative twists and turns. In his case, they eased many of the concerns he had about the welfare of employees and clients.

"The biggest thing I see people do wrong with mergers and acquisitions is they let emotion become the driver," he says. "And the non-negotiable list takes a lot of emotion out of the equation."

Another lesson was the importance of communication that avoids false expectations.

"The big mistakes are often related to assumptions that get made. And that's often [because of] not taking the time to have the necessary conversations—just assuming things will be a particular way. You've got to make sure you really understand what's going to happen."

Arlin also believes it's vital to plan for a sale long before selling—"at least three years"—and financially run the business so that it's *ready* to sell, even if a deal isn't in the works. Additionally, he advises business owners to build a team of qualified people to help them through an agreement, including lawyers, accountants, and M&A advisers.

"Don't go cheap. I see many people who try to do it on their own or cut corners everywhere they can. It is not the time to do that when you're trying to make the biggest sale of your career. You want to have the right resources, and they do cost money—but it's worth it."

Finally, there is the crucial lesson mentioned at the beginning of this case study: business owners should plan what to do next.

"I still vividly remember a young kid that had amazing success and sold his business for more money than he ever dreamed of having. A year after the sale, I had him speak to a group, and he started his speech with, 'I've never had a more miserable year in my life. I have all the money I could ever hope for, and I am as lost and miserable as I could ever be.' Because he had no purpose. So, he eventually started another company."

Arlin has thankfully avoided this fate.

"I haven't slowed down a whole lot, working for ConnectWise pretty much full time and then doing these other things on the side. But I've been doing that my entire career," he says. "The serial entrepreneurial part of me says never, ever quit. Just keep on coming up with ideas and give it a try."

Dave Cava
and Proactive Technologies

Dave Cava became an entrepreneur almost by accident. Like many founders, he wound up in a job that he could do better without his employer, and he and a partner decided to strike out on their own. Dave began with no clients and little funding, betting everything—including the house—on the startup. Over the next 11 years, the partners built a successful managed IT services company that served the financial services industry in New York City.

Along the way, the founders received numerous casual offers to buy, seriously considering two. One deal came close, but Dave and his partner did what many sellers can't: they walked away. And a subsequent offer years later wound up being the right one at precisely the right time.

The business had encountered new scaling challenges, and Dave was faced with a tragic family illness. When it was time to move on, he fortunately found a buyer who enabled him to do it well.

The roots of accidental entrepreneurship

Dave trained in theology, and his first job was as a pastor in Brooklyn. When he amicably left that position at 27 years old, he was married, had an infant daughter, and was paying $1,200 a month in rent with only about $2,000 in the bank. Some soul-searching about what to do with his life led him to IT—he was good with computers. So, he took a temporary job working night security and studied for his first computer certification on the job.

Dave scored his first tech position at a dot.com that failed, and he bounced around several jobs before landing with a consulting company in 2002. So much work had dried up in New York City after 9-11 that the company started taking on any work it could, including network support contracts that were outside its expertise. The experiment was failing, with four unprofitable clients who were ready to walk. So, Dave's bosses gave him two techs, pointed him at the problem, and told him to fix it. He believed that "if we didn't start making money after a month, they were going to fire us all."

Within five years, the network support group had about 30 clients and almost $2 million in revenue, becoming the largest part of the consultancy. But while Dave liked the work, he wasn't happy in a "dysfunctional" environment. So, he approached his boss, said he was leaving, and asked the man to partner up in a new business.

In 2007, Proactive Technologies was born.

Rapid growth aided by specialization

Dave and his partner funded the venture with $50,000 apiece, with much of the money coming from home equity lines of credit on their houses. They had no Plan B.

"We saw this as succeed or lose our houses," Dave recalls.

The partners attempted to buy the existing contracts from their employer and failed. But they'd informed the clients they were leaving, so they simply waited. Sure enough, some felt the pain quickly and approached them to handle network support. And after being sued by and settling with their former employer, the business took off.

Proactive Technologies grew to $1.4 million in revenue and 12 employees within eight months. Dave believes that the key to this growth was their choice to specialize in a vertical market. Proactive Technologies focused on serving the financial services industry, specifically hedge funds and private equity firms in New York City.

"It really propelled our business," Dave says. "All of a sudden, we're competing against two or three companies instead of a hundred."

Another critical move was an evolution into managed services and monthly recurring revenue (MRR). At first, the company provided the same network support they'd done for clients at the previous employer—managed IT services were still in their infancy. But Dave and his partner made a concerted push toward flat fees as this became a viable business model.

The interest in buying his business grew along with it, and Dave ignored these overtures for seven years. But in 2014, one of them caught his attention.

"You get approached by prospective buyers a lot when you own this kind of business. But this one seemed like it might be a real opportunity," he says.

A possible sale and pulling the plug

Proactive Technologies had hit about $3 million in revenue by then, and Dave and his partner thought about selling for various reasons.

First, there was a scaling challenge. The MSP had grown to 24 employees, but Dave realized that they'd never really broken through the common small-business barrier of "10 guys and an owner." They were really *that* company, only with two owners and a bigger team. Proactive had no middle management between the founders and front-line employees. It was "stuck" at this level, and Dave knew that it would take a major effort to grow.

Then, there was the thought of cashing out and living life again. The money was decent, and the idea of actually getting ROI on the effort was appealing. In addition, the pressure of running a business never seemed to go away.

"The first year in business, you're like, 'This is so crazy. I can't possibly keep up this pace,'" Dave says. "You tell yourself things will calm down, and it'll be nice when these challenges are over. But after a while, it dawns on you that while you may be able to get some things under control, those hurdles never really stop for a small business owner until you're much bigger."

Dave and his partner signed non-disclosure agreements (NDAs) with the prospective buyer, made it through due diligence, and were on the verge of receiving a letter of intent (LOI) to buy the company. As they discussed terms, Dave and his partner told the buyer they'd sell if a few hundred thousand more dollars were guaranteed instead of a conditional earn-out. The business broker who managed the deal was a "slick salesman type" who told them "no problem." But then the LOI showed up.

"He sent us this LOI that was no different," Dave says. "We said, 'thanks for making that decision easy for us. No, we're not going to do this.' I said to my partner, 'It just doesn't feel right. It feels like we've got all kinds of unfinished business.'"

Despite getting excited about "more money than I'd ever seen in my life," Dave and his partner walked away from the deal. They didn't trust the broker or the terms and thought Proactive Technologies was "on the brink of potentially exploding."

As it turns out, they were right.

Solving scalability issues leads to accelerated growth

Proactive nearly tripled its revenue over the next four years. But doing it wasn't easy. Dave and his partner had to solve the scalability problem by putting the pieces in place to delegate. This effort required changing operations and processes, building middle management, and some hard decisions.

"We had a lot of employees who had been around a long time, and they were used to only reporting to an owner," Dave explains. "So, we had to either have some people get with the program or move on. That was very painful because they were some of our favorite people, some of whom had been with us from the beginning."

The hard transition succeeded. It took the company seven years to hit $3 million in revenue, but only four and a half more to crest $10 million.

This growth created new issues, however, and they started at the top. Dave and his partner worked well together and had survived the business curse of being equal partners, an arrangement with an average failure rate nearing 80%. But expanding further now required a single leader. [2]

"We needed one person running the company. And we weren't sure it was either of us," Dave says. "I also functioned as the COO/CFO with no formal finance training. We were at about 45 employees and $10 million, so getting to the next level would be very challenging and require some major changes. So, we thought about selling."

Fortunately, some other MSPs had a lot of money to throw around. By 2018, private equity firms had taken a keen interest in the managed services space, especially businesses that served the financial services vertical.

"All of a sudden, our larger competitors suddenly had access to cash they'd never had before," Dave says. "So, as we're poised for

---

2   Levin Marissa. "The 5 Nonnegotiable Factors of Any Successful Partnership." Inc. https://www.inc.com/marissa-levin/the-5-most-important-strategies-for-creating-a-successful-business-partnership.html

consolidation, they had the capital. And they needed something to do with it."

The scalability challenges and this opportunity meant it was a great time to sell. But shocking family news soon made it *necessary*. In 2018, Dave's 14-year-old daughter Gabby was diagnosed with Metastatic Signet Ring Cell Carcinoma, an incredibly rare and aggressive form of colon cancer.

"The doctors told us there had only been 35 pediatric cases, and none of them had survived. They basically said her chances were zero or close to it," Dave recalls. "A surgeon told us, 'Whatever you had going on in your life before; this takes over *everything*.'"

Gabby quickly underwent a difficult surgery and faced a terrible prognosis, but she and her family were determined to fight.

"The prognosis is grim. We're going to need a miracle," Dave wrote at the time. "Gabby is awesome. She has cancer. She is tough, and so are we, and God is good no matter what."

Looking for a buyer

Dave and his partner never put out a "for sale" sign. Instead, they sifted through the regular inquires and quickly found one worth considering.

Another managed services provider was looking to break into the financial services vertical. The prospect had capital, and the numbers they discussed were great, but Dave and his partner got the sense the company would lay off a lot of employees and lose a lot of their clients. The partners couldn't live with that, so they canceled the deal just before a letter of intent.

"We'd walk away rich, but it's going to be hard to look people in the eye and tell them we were selling," Dave explains. "Because we knew (the buyer would) screw the company up."

Dave and his partner contacted a second MSP staked by a private equity firm and told the owners they were getting offers, commenting that the two companies would be "a good fit." It was a soft approach, but it worked. The overture was made in June 2018, and the deal closed in the following January.

The process wasn't easy, however. The two companies "danced" for months during tricky negotiations.

The due diligence process was extensive, and the prospective buyer expressed a few concerns after some analysis. Similar to the acquisition attempt Dave and his partner had spurned years back, the question of what percentage of the deal was guaranteed and what portion would be contingent on a conditional earnout became a sticking point. And the issue threatened to derail the deal.

Dave and his partner knew that while most owners assume they'll get 90% of any earn-out money, the actual number is usually significantly lower. They wanted a better deal. So, the partners decided to cool off the negotiations for a while and hope the buyer would revise their approach.

"It was terrifying," Dave recalls. "The whole thing is a courtship, like trying to establish boundaries in a relationship. So, you say, 'That's something I'm not gonna stand for.' But then you go home and pray they don't break up with you."

Fortunately, this young relationship had a chaperone. The private equity firm with a stake in the buying company called both parties up to their offices to see if they could "hash things out."

A compromise with an upside

Needless to say, Dave and his partner were a bundle of nerves going into that meeting. But they knew that everyone wanted the deal to happen, were willing to compromise, and felt like they came up with a fair and reasonable proposal. Both sides gave a little and walked out that day shaking hands on a revised deal structure. Dave and his partner agreed to put some money at risk by hitting revenue targets, but they wanted a chance for the upside, too.

"Even though we knew it was a longshot that we'd beat those revenue targets, we wanted to know we'd be rewarded if we did," Dave says. "All we asked for was the chance to bet on ourselves, as we had done from the beginning."

"The agreement was a giant relief. But we were still very reluctant to count our chickens. There was still due diligence going on and many things that could have gone wrong."

These worries weren't realized, however. Several months later, the deal closed successfully—the sale went through at an EBITDA multiple that was far higher than the "going rate" at that time. He attributes this valuation to the following factors:

- The acquisition was a strategic buy of a relatively large company.

- The two MSPs shared standard technologies that fit perfectly.

- Proactive Technologies had a high proportion of monthly recurring revenue from stable clients.

⁂ Crucially, Proactive served the financial services vertical, and so did the buyer. This specialization was uncommon and therefore valuable.

An emotional roller coaster

Dave was relieved and happy with the deal. But on the same day he signed the closing documents, his wife Audra sat in an oncologist's office, learning that their daughter's cancer had returned.

When Gabby was first diagnosed, the prognosis was terrible. But the family fought the odds, and treatment had stalled her tumor markers for a time. Nevertheless, Gabby could only take so much chemotherapy, and Dave's wife learned the cancer was growing again on the day the sale completed. Audra didn't tell him this news immediately, however. She wanted to spare him the pain in the middle of a milestone achievement.

"She said to me, 'This is a once-in-a-lifetime thing you just did. And I wanted you to be able to enjoy it,'" Dave says. "I told her I was so grateful … and also 'please don't *ever* do that again.'"

Within a week of signing, Dave told his new employers that he couldn't work as much as planned. They were understanding—another reason it wound up being the right deal.

"The buyer was great to me. They really gave me a lot of flexibility and were better to me than they had to be," Dave says.

He was free to do what needed to be done, and the following year was an odyssey of medical treatments, travel, and shared family struggle and bonding. In April, Gabby endured a 19-hour surgery that removed many of her organs and washed out her insides with Hyperthermic Intraperitoneal Chemotherapy ("hot chemo"). The procedure was drastic but certainly worth it.

"It bought her another eight and a half months that were wonderful," Dave says. "We spent a chunk of that time traveling together, running around getting treatments in Germany, trying to experiment with interventions they couldn't do here."

Dave is "forever grateful" for getting out of the business when he did and the opportunity to spend time with his daughter. Gabrielle Velouria Cava passed away peacefully and surrounded by family on January 12, 2020, at the age of 16.

"When Gabby was diagnosed, they gave her nine months to live. But she made it 21," Dave says. "She was a super-tough, super-positive kid who was full of faith and wasn't scared to die. She was incredible. Just an *incredible* kid."

Lessons learned in life and business

The emotions that come along with selling a business pale in comparison to a family's tragedy. But Dave learned they are there—and significant. He experienced the fear of setting boundaries and walking away. Then, there was the anxiety over what due diligence might reveal. And not telling his employees about a sale while trying to protect their jobs was hard.

"They start to hear rumors and ask if you're selling, which was challenging," he says. "We'd just tell them we routinely get offers, and if it's a good one, we'd consider it—but not do anything that would put our clients or employees in a bad situation. So, you answer the question without answering."

"What employees *really* want to know is 'do I need to start looking for another job?' So, if you can honestly let them know that they *don't* without directly revealing a sale, it's a good way to handle things."

As for other advice to business owners, Dave cautions them to straighten out their books and be practical about valuation and expectations.

"The way you do your books, the way you pay yourself, the way you book revenue, the way you try and sell—the accounting piece of it is way more important to maximizing value than most people realize. For example, it's a basic thing, but recurring revenue is *far* more valuable than an equivalent number in hourly work or consulting sales."

Ultimately, Dave thinks owners should streamline accounting and get a realistic picture of a business's market value while understanding that even *that* number may be off.

"Any buyer worth their salt is going to do some real due diligence," Dave warns. "And their valuation isn't going to be based on the numbers you put in front of them. It's going to be based on the numbers that they draw out."

Dave also firmly believes that a business should specialize, if possible, and that this early decision was crucial to Proactive Technologies' growth and its high valuation.

"You want your company to be known as the best at something, whether that's a vertical focus or a technology focus. It becomes so much more attractive as an acquisition target."

Finally, Dave cautions sellers to prepare for the aftermath of a sale. His situation is unusual, as he sold the business that consumed his professional life for 12 years and experienced a tragic loss simultaneously. Nevertheless, Dave believes every business owner who lacks a plan for what to do next will encounter difficult soul-searching.

"I'm at this bizarre inflection point in my life where act one is over, and act two hasn't started," he says. "I lost my daughter and sold my business at the same time, and then there was the pandemic. Now, I've got time and money. But I'm still trying to figure out what to do with the rest of my life—which is good in some ways, but also stressful."

"My identity was very much as a business owner. So, the struggle to figure out what to do next is a very real thing, and it's compounded because of what happened with my family."

Dave believes that his future *might* involve building another business.

"When I started my first business, I had a pit in my stomach—I was just terrified. I started it because things were falling apart at the company I was at. It wasn't something I was excited about; it was just the right move. I did It with my head, not my heart. But now that I have a successful business behind me and won't be risking my house, the idea seems kind of fun. We'll see."

Robert Lindley and Innovative Systems, Inc.

Robert Lindley can look back on a very long career and entrepreneurial journey. He sold his only business 37 years after first working in information technology and 23 years after founding the company.

Robert recently entered retirement full-time and rediscovered his purpose, but only after a struggle resolved by dedicated thought and planning. A big part of him misses the total engagement of entrepreneurship, even though he's glad to be done with its challenges.

Over more than two decades of business ownership, Robert experienced many classic founder issues and organizational pivots. But he also hit some less common emotional lows—many of them driven by his failed attempts at succession planning.

Early entrepreneurship

Robert decided to become an entrepreneur after the software development company he worked for started sending him all over the country to install software. Even more travel was in the cards, so he resigned and started a business in 1994.

For the first five years, Innovative Systems, Inc. was a one-person shop providing software development consulting. Robert hired his first employee in 1999, followed by a couple of others, in what he recalls as a "fun" period—few employees, low overhead, and not many policies. But the challenges grew as the business did, and Robert was the classic example of an inexperienced entrepreneur described in Michael Gerber's book *The E-Myth*. He was simply a technician hiring other technicians and had "no idea how to be a business owner."

The reckoning came in 2004, when Robert's first employee—later, his son-in-law—left the business to work with one of its clients. The man saw little future at the firm, as it wasn't expanding, and cash flow was always a near-run thing.

"It was a big wake-up call," Robert says. "I was like, 'What am I doing?' I was not running it like a business; it was a job."

Righting the ship (and righting it again)

Things changed radically from 2005 on. Robert hired his first office administrator, moved the operation out of his house and leased office space, and, crucially, joined a business peer group. Robert's fellow IT entrepreneurs at Heartland Technology Group (HTG) taught him "how to become a manager and think like a business owner."

Robert eventually implemented new processes and created sales and service manager positions that removed him "as the bottleneck" to getting things done. As a result, the business flourished, evolving into a managed IT services provider (MSP) that catered to professional services firms. But when the economy stalled in 2010, the company experienced more cash flow issues. While Robert had vastly improved operations, he hadn't paid enough attention to the business's financial aspects.

"It was my second wake-up call," Robert says. "And thinking about the finances led me to think about what we were doing and why we were doing it."

Robert and his team weathered the cash-flow crisis by streamlining the company's books, and they also defined a robust culture, core values, and purpose. Innovative Systems was back on track by 2012, and it was a *better* company.

Nevertheless, the struggle to get there had been the "second low point" in Robert's entrepreneurial career.

Stability and failed succession planning

By 2014, Innovative Systems had become very profitable while growing to nearly $2 million in revenue and 13 employees. The MSP celebrated its 20th anniversary as Robert turned 58, and he started seriously considering exit planning.

"At that age, you start thinking, 'Hey, this isn't going to last forever,'" Robert says.

He decided the best exit plan involved passing on the business to his key employees. So, he designed a 12-year buyout plan and presented it to his longtime sales and service managers. It was essentially an employee stock program that required the two men to sign three-year commitments. Upon signing, they would gain a portion of company stock, followed by four additional stock buys at three-year intervals. The two employees' salaries were set at a fair amount, and none of the stock buys were out-of-pocket—each would be funded by performance-based pay tied to the company's profits.

Unfortunately, the plan didn't go over well.

Both potential successors were surprised by the offer and couldn't see past the risk if the business struggled. They also had concerns over their base pay, having a stake but little decision-making authority, and the company's discretionary spending. But the *risk* was the primary issue.

"They had a salary, and they liked it. And they didn't have exposure to the risk I'd been taking for years by starting and running a business," Robert recalls. "I should have bounced the idea off of my peer group before introducing it. They could have told me what the team's reaction was going to be—and later did—and I was stupid."

"But I was really close to these men, and they'd been working with me a long time," he continues. "I thought, 'Hey, here I am offering to sell a multimillion-dollar company with no money out of their pocket, and that's a good deal.' Yet they came back with conditions, and it kind of upset me. But [looking back], I totally understand their concerns—and I should have been well-prepared."

Robert shelved the buyout plan and instead rolled out a 20% variable-compensation plan tied to achieving key performance indicators (KPIs). The company would pay the two employees generously if they hit those benchmarks. Robert also hoped that they'd be open to a future buyout agreement once they started achieving the objectives.

A family tragedy, emotional exhaustion, and the decision to sell

While Robert's service manager hit all of his KPIs in 2015, his sales manager of 12 years didn't and decided to leave the company in January of 2016. And the month before, Robert's son Chris died of a heart attack at the age of 32. Chris had been born with a heart defect, but the family wasn't aware of any recent medical issues when he died. His death was a shock, and this sudden tragedy and losing his longtime sales manager spurred Robert to reflect on his past and future.

"When I think back through my history, I had a son-in-law who wasn't interested in the business and didn't see a future. And I've had two men who were like sons [the sales and service managers] I've grown with and mentored, and *they* didn't see a future owning the business. And now, I've lost my son—followed by my other 'son' resigning. So I was just emotionally and mentally exhausted."

Robert was faced with reengineering his business amid this fatigue, and he started to worry about catastrophe if his service manager left, too.

Robert and his wife, Deborah, spent two days with a peer group leader and completed a "life plan" in 2016 that clarified a few things. First, he'd been doing some business coaching on the side and realized that he enjoyed that work a great deal more than running the company. In addition, he determined that managing the business in its current stage didn't feel right anymore—it was dragging him down.

Robert had a heart-to-heart with his remaining key employee, the service manager, about succession. But the two men determined that any deal would require external financing, a situation that puts intense pressure on a new owner. Robert finally decided it was time to sell to an outside party.

Finding buyers and evaluating offers

Like many owners of MSPs, Robert didn't have to work hard to find prospective buyers. Two years earlier, the owners of a local copier company had expressed interest in buying Innovative Systems, so he simply re-engaged with them. At the same time—the third quarter of 2016—a second copier company in town made overtures.

Robert signed mutual non-disclosure agreements (NDAs) with both prospects, followed by providing preliminary assessments of his company's financials. While he didn't tell most of his employees the business was for sale, he did involve his longtime service manager throughout the process.

Robert soon had two letters in hand: a letter of intent (LOI) from one company that included an approximate offer and a demand for exclusivity and a letter of engagement (LOE) that requested a third-party assessment of the MSP's value.

Robert agreed to the LOE conditions and quickly retained a valuation consultant who both parties trusted. He also assembled a "dream team," including his outsourced CFO, his CPA, his attorney, and a financial planner, to help define his personal needs:

- Robert wanted a secure retirement for him and his wife until 90 years old and healthcare coverage until 65.

- He didn't want to sell and become a full-time employee just to keep health insurance.

- He wanted the buyer to maintain Innovative Systems' staff, treat his service manager right, and serve existing clients well.

- The sale must present a minimal risk for both him and the buyer.

Simultaneously, the valuation consultant conducted due diligence and outlined some pros and cons of the MSP. While Innovative Systems had no growth in the previous year, served a "tier-three market," and had an understaffed sales department, the evaluator judged the company's management and financials—from processes to margins—"best in class." The resulting valuation was where Robert thought it would be: a 6.5 multiple of earnings before interest, taxes, depreciation, and amortization (EBITDA).

Robert received a second letter of intent from the prospect who had first given him the LOE. But after reviewing it, he decided the deal would not meet his conditional list. The possible buyer might shed employees, clients would need to adopt new technology, and Robert's service manager would be in a lesser position. So he rejected the LOI and showed the other buyer the third-party valuation. That deal was a better fit:

- The offer was a stock purchase that met Robert's retirement goals.

- It included Robert remaining on salary as an employee with healthcare coverage until 65, but his role would only be consulting.

- Because the MSP would become a new division of the copier company, the deal retained employees, elevated the service manager, and maintained the same technology and services for clients.

Robert signed this letter of intent.

Deal details and surprises

Robert was excited and relieved to sign the LOI and had high hopes for the deal.

"I'd known the buyer's family for over 35 years, and we went to church with them," he says. "So, I knew their culture as a family-owned business. I saw the possibility of meeting all my objectives—not just financially, but keeping employees and clients happy, and the business intact."

Nevertheless, Robert had some worries during the due diligence period. He was concerned about a more detailed assessment of the financials and whether the buyer and his loyal service manager would get along.

"I was hoping it would be a good fit, but I was honestly more concerned with what my service manager thought of the buyer rather than what they thought of him," Robert says. "And about a month into due diligence, I got a little anxious after they asked for copies of our QuickBooks files and a ton of other things. Was there anything I missed?"

Fortunately, the service manager and the buyer got along well. And the CPA who reviewed Innovative Systems' financials said, "I wish our books were this clean." After three months of due diligence, the contract was signed.

"I was relieved and excited," Robert said.

The nuts and bolts of the deal

In contrast to the tentative offer by the other company, which was an asset purchase, the deal Robert chose was a stock purchase.

There was technically no performance-based earn-out portion to Robert's payment, which was 75% upfront and the balance paid over the next 57 months with interest. The company agreed to keep him on the payroll as a salaried consultant with full health insurance for him and his wife and 401k benefits for this period. There was, however, an "offset" clause in the deal. If the buyer later discovered any financial or operational surprises that financially impacted the MSP, they had the right to address the issue and renegotiate the promissory note to Robert.

"There was still some risk in this offset clause," Robert says. "But I knew how complete everything I'd provided them was, so I was confident."

One wrinkle to the deal stemmed from the MSP having always run on cash vs. credit, so there was a substantial balance in the firm's bank account. Robert had already paid taxes on the funds, and the financials proved that the business didn't need all that money to run well. So, the parties created a formula to define appropriate working capital after the sale, and Robert eventually recouped most of those funds.

The aftermath and advice to other entrepreneurs

Throughout the sale, Robert's wife Deborah had one primary concern: what would he do with his life after selling the business? Based on Robert's love for helping others, the plan was to focus on being a facilitator for his IT peer group and perhaps another Christian-based peer group. But once the deal was signed, the couple had an epiphany.

"Wait a minute; we don't have to do these things unless we want to!" Robert says. "We realized that we had an opportunity to take a year or two and figure out what's next."

Robert and Deborah had always loved travel, mixing mini-vacations with business trips over the years. So, the couple paused Robert's plans to coach, purchased a 40-foot motorhome, and began traveling the country. Unfortunately, Deborah suffered a stroke early in their journey, and they stopped traveling during her recovery. But the couple stayed in the RV, Deborah's health improved, and they resumed travel for much of the following year. Robert and Deborah drove 21,000 miles and visited countless friends and family while hitting 32 states, Canada, and 15 national parks.

Sadly, Deborah's long-term health took a turn for the worse in 2020, just as the pandemic hit. She was diagnosed with vascular dementia caused by the stroke, and extensive travel was no longer possible as Robert looked after her health. Faced with this challenge amid COVID lockdowns, he started thinking about his future. He'd planned to go back to business facilitation and coaching, but that simply wasn't realistic anymore.

"I was really struggling. It's like my whole life didn't have purpose anymore," he says. "So, I went back and revisited my life plan, and that's what helped get me back out of the trench and figure out what's next."

This is the biggest lesson Robert wants to communicate to other entrepreneurs considering a sale: **figure out your purpose and what fulfills you, and plan what to do next.**

"I think for too many of us entrepreneurs, the business is all we do," he says. "And man, what a hole to fill."

Robert also has advice for owners who consider mixing business with family, whether it's their traditional family or the individuals who become *like* family. In retrospect, he understands why his son-in-law left the company many years ago and turned down a subsequent, soft overture to buy it. And his other "sons"— the sales and service managers—imparted additional lessons by turning down his buyout plan.

"There are risks trying to pass on a business to people you care about, and one of them is that the business competes with your relationships," Robert says. "For example, the 12-year buyout that my employees rejected would have created a tremendous amount of risk for me compared to the eventual sale. And my son-in-law was also very smart about *his* decisions."

"I've seen some sales in my peer group that were family deals that did not go very well," he continues. "One big problem is that the buyer personally finances a deal, and if the business fails after the transfer, not only did it fail, but the seller must then decide to get back into the business or lose money needed for retirement."

Robert also believes owners actively looking to sell should assess potential buyers and consider *their* needs when making decisions. For example, Robert didn't replace the sales manager who left because both of his prospects already had this position filled. Not only would the training, salary, and benefits for a new sales manager have been a waste, but he would have made that person's continued employment a condition of a sale—which would have made both deals impossible.

"We ultimately sold the business for close to 7.5 times EBITDA. So, a sales manager's salary of an extra $100,000 would have lowered the sale price by about $750,000," he reflects. "And us not replacing that role is a big reason we were able to sell in the first place."

Nevertheless, Robert's most important piece of advice remains "decide what you plan to do next." After selling, Deborah's health issues and the pandemic lockdowns meant that he had to rediscover his purpose. He found that he could be a family historian, a photographer, and woodworker while taking care of his wife at home. Sadly, Deborah passed away in October 2021. So, he is back reviewing his life plan to decide "what's next."

In the end, Robert achieves perspective through detailed life planning summarized by a simple but powerful statement:

"I have not retired from life; I have just retired from the things in life that I no longer want to do!"

Brett Jaffe and His IT Services Firm

B rett Jaffe is a strategic business coach who also serves as the CEO of a software company. In his coaching role, he helps other entrepreneurs tackle many of the challenges he encountered as a business owner and avoid some of his mistakes.

"I help businesses with multiple facets, from strategy and execution to legacy and life planning," Brett says. "It's great being able to convey some of my past experiences and channel them into a business model that truly helps others."

Many of the issues Brett had in his earlier days as an owner are common for inexperienced entrepreneurs, including a lack of business knowledge and insufficient planning. But one problem proved to be virtually unsolvable: an incompatible partnership. Two equal partners' differing visions for the company eventually caused Brett to sell his stake.

Brett's story ultimately has a happy ending, as he sold successfully and moved on to bigger and better things. But the partnership conflicts caused tension for about a decade, and the year Brett sold was the most stressful experience of his life.

Accidental entrepreneurship after calling an audible on medicine

Brett graduated from Tufts University in 1992 and was set to enter a five-year program to achieve a combined medical degree and master's degree in public health. But then he started to have doubts about this career path. Brett would have to take out massive student loans, and he realized he'd be almost 40 years old before his training was over.

He loved building and troubleshooting computers—it was a longtime hobby, and he "had a knack for it." So, Brett deferred his entry into the MD/Master's program for a year and took a job doing tech support at a software company to put some money in his pocket. Simultaneously, he reached out to a man he knew who ran a part-time small business that assembled and sold desktop PCs. Brett pitched the idea of teaching DOS and Microsoft Windows classes to the man's customers. The owner agreed and soon asked Brett if he wanted to do more for the company. Brett wound up buying in as a minority partner for a "token fee" and, within a year, he'd left his other job to become its first full-time employee.

At the time, the business was reselling parts and assembling computers sold out of a small retail storefront. But many business customers started asking for more advanced support and consulting, and the company soon became an IT services provider as Brett and his partner realized it was a better business model. Eventually, the business evolved into a dedicated managed IT services provider (MSP) with recurring revenue.

Within a couple of years, Brett's partner gave him the remaining 20% stake to become a 50/50 partner, recognizing the hard work that was largely responsible for the company's success. It was an incredible opportunity in a business Brett loved. But the informal arrangement with no proactive planning set the stage for later troubles.

Learning how to be a business owner

Like many sudden entrepreneurs, Brett and his partner were doing something they liked and were good at, but they had little idea how to run a business. Neither man knew how to devise a marketing plan, create profit and loss statements, outline long-term goals, or make projections.

"It was a lot of fun, but we didn't have any focus on the big picture," Brett recalls. "I could keep the books straight enough for us to be profitable, but there was no strategy whatsoever. Fortunately, at that time, you could almost run a computer company and make money by accident."

This business free-for-all lasted most of the company's first 10 years. The MSP grew and made money but got most of the clients through referrals, and the partners had to evolve a profitable pricing and services strategy after several failed approaches. Eventually, Brett resolved to learn the entrepreneurial ropes. He joined a local peer group, started reading business books and other resources, and began implementing the core components of a well-designed business. In retrospect, Brett regrets that these changes happened so late.

"I feel like if we'd went into this business intentionally—making sure we hired the right people, having the right culture, having some kind of a long-term vision and running it with metrics—we'd have been in a much different position," he says. "The business would have been much more valuable, and a lot of what eventually happened may have been different."

Many of the changes improved the MSP, and it continued to grow. But eventually, this progress hit a wall. Taking the company to the next level was hampered by the partners having different visions, and an unequal work environment caused simmering resentment to boil over.

The hazards of equal partnership

By the early 2000s, the company was doing pretty well and had improved some of the fundamentals. But most of the strategic moves, client relationships, marketing strategies, and other vital elements were handled by Brett.

Brett and his partner had always rationalized that Brett was given the remaining shares for an equal stake with the expectation he would be the one growing the company. But after a decade of work, Brett started to realize it was an inequitable relationship. In addition, the two men had radically incompatible ideas of what to do with the firm. Brett wanted to systematically grow it into something much bigger. But his partner was 10 years older and viewed the business more as a cash resource that essentially ran fine as it was.

"It seemed we were almost spinning our wheels. The bigger the business got, the more money he took out of it, making it harder to invest in the company," Brett says. "For example, we could have reinvested some of that profit into hiring more personnel who would help us grow, and both of us would have been better for it."

The conflict first boiled over nearing the business's 10-year mark, just before Brett got married in 2001. Several tense conversations blew up into an argument followed by an awkward working relationship. The two men eventually got over the dispute, and Brett's partner allowed him to make some strategic and financial moves without micromanaging the effort. Among the changes, Brett hired a business coach to help with strategy and execution, and he learned invaluable lessons about running a business. As a result, the company's structure, processes, team, and marketing improved, and this investment paid off in significant growth. Within a few years, the MSP hit revenue of $5 million in an industry where cracking $2 million was difficult.

The company also spun off several businesses from its core managed IT services: the partners founded forensic hardware and electronic discovery companies in 2007 and started a cloud services business in 2011. Nevertheless, the partnership issues and hard feelings persisted and grew over the years.

"I was the one thinking strategically and working nights and weekends," Brett says. "There started to be a lot of animosity because I was essentially doing 90% of the work for the same salary and 50% of the profit. And that eats at you after a while."

Working at cross-purposes

Brett's partner was relatively hands-off for a time, allowing Brett to put many strategic and tactical improvements in place. But he was still an equal partner and eventually made decisions that directly conflicted with Brett's.

For example, Brett created a new incentive plan to reward and retain employees while motivating them to hit key performance indicators (KPIs). But when he left for a couple of days to attend an event, his partner told the employees that the program wasn't in effect and did something else with the money. This clash and other conflicts started creating an environment where employees had to choose sides. And the fact that many of Brett's partner's family members worked for the company complicated matters.

"It just wasn't healthy," Brett says. "So, I came back from a conference in 2011, and I was just done. I gave him an ultimatum: 'Listen—one of us has to go. Either I buy you out, or you buy me out.'"

Brett suggested they take 30 days to think of a plan but specified that the deal must be completed within a year. His partner took the ultimatum calmly but not exactly well.

Valuation struggles and structuring a deal

Ultimately, the only option that made sense and had a real chance of success was Brett's partner buying him out. For example, some of the partner's family members were employees, and he was about 10 years older than Brett and couldn't see himself doing anything after ownership. In contrast, Brett was younger and had other options.

"I think he saw the business as kind of a cash cow. It was making money, and he could do whatever he wanted; buy nice cars and put money in the bank. He was just at a different stage of life," Brett says. "I was working my butt off and in the office every day, whereas if he didn't show up for a month, it wouldn't affect us. So, there was just a lot of resentment over the inequity of the effort and compensation. And it was frustrating not being able to do some of the things that would grow the business and make it even more valuable."

Nevertheless, selling his stake in the business wasn't a clean solution that would end all of this stress. Brett was convinced the company wouldn't survive too long without his involvement, so any deal with a long earn-out period carried significant risk. And while Brett had recommended putting in place a detailed buy-sell agreement years ago, Brett's partner had rejected the idea. Thus, there was no formal structure for an exit. This ambiguity caused new arguments—and some of them were petty.

"His attitude was, 'Hey, I gave you a percentage of the business years ago. If you want to walk away, then you don't get anything for it,'" Brett says. "I think he somewhat felt betrayed that I wanted to leave."

Walking away without appropriate compensation was a non-starter, of course. Brett proposed bringing in a third-party company within the IT industry to conduct a valuation. But his partner countered that he'd already provided the books to an accountant friend of his and received a valuation. Predictably, it was a pretty low number.

"He obviously wanted a much lower valuation because he was buying it. And I wanted a fair valuation because I was selling it," Brett says. "So, that's a really big challenge when a partner sells to the other one without a proactive agreement in place."

Brett approached this impasse strategically. He offered to buy his partner out at about three times the low valuation that the partner had proposed. Both men knew that if the matter ever went to arbitration or court, the third party would probably settle the dispute by choosing the deal offered by the highest bidder. Thus, Brett would wind up buying his partner out at the higher valuation, and the partner didn't want that—he was forced to compromise.

"We eventually came up with something that I knew was a fair price," Brett says. "I said, 'It's lower than I would have received if we sold it to someone else. But it's higher than what your accountant friend says it is. And here's the difference.'"

Brett's partner couldn't afford to buy him out all at once, so Brett would receive 25% upfront and 75% paid out in monthly installments over three years. The structure involved significant risk since Brett was leaving the company and had essentially run everything, but it was a compromise he felt he had to make to get the sale going. And by that point, the relationship had gotten so unhealthy that Brett "just wanted to walk away."

In addition, Brett would retain 100% of the cloud services company they'd started the year before. Since the partner wasn't involved in this business and it had little revenue at the time, he didn't mind letting it go. And building that business had long been part of Brett's exit plan.

The partners had their shared business attorney draft the agreement, and each of their personal lawyers reviewed the draft and tweaked the language until all parties were satisfied. When he finally signed the contract, Brett felt more concern than relief. He was worried about issues that might crop up with the payments over the next three years. He also fretted over what he would do next after leaving the company he'd been consumed by for 20 years.

The aftermath of letting go

Some of Brett's worries about the deal were justified—a subsequent conflict endangered him getting paid the total sum he was owed. But he successfully navigated these issues with legal help and eventually received the money. After a six-month transition period in which Brett stayed on and documented every relevant process, password, and operational detail, he completely detached himself from the business.

Brett immediately went to work for OS33, a software company that acquired his cloud services business and engaged him to build it as a reseller channel. Unfettered from the constraints in his former working relationship, Brett grew the new division to nearly $30 million in revenue over the next five years.

"I had doubted myself after essentially running a business handcuffed," Brett says. "But building the cloud division gave me a lot of fulfillment that I could build a program from scratch successfully. And they treated me really well."

The day the last check from the sale of his partnership stake cleared, Brett's "stress level dropped to the floor." And because he'd received these payments while working for the other company, his financial security had never been better. Nevertheless, the year of the sale had taken a toll, and it still ranks as the worst period of his life.

Advice to other entrepreneurs

Brett's hard lessons form the basis of his most important piece of advice to other entrepreneurs who are considering a partnership or currently in one.

"It would have been a thousand percent easier to sell to an outside party, or if we had a proactive, written purchase and sale agreement," Brett says. "So, the biggest lesson is to address the 'what if' situations before they become 'what if' situations. For example, what if a partner dies or is incapacitated? Who takes over ownership decisions? And, of course, how will a deal work if a partner wants to leave—financing, valuation, and payment terms?"

Brett has other regrets about his experience, but they are mixed with his practical judgment that perhaps some of the pain was necessary. It was all part of a valuable business education.

"I feel a bit of frustration thinking about the fact that I should have exited the company a decade before instead of doing things handcuffed [to a partner]," Brett says. "But I did grow that MSP to $5 million in revenue, which is not easy to do and something I'm proud of. Also, I don't think I was mentally ready to take the next step a decade before. Yes, it was 10 more years of frustration but also 10 more years of learning."

Brett doesn't think all 50/50 partnerships are bad ideas, though he's seen many of them experience issues in his work as a business coach. To do the relationship right, Brett believes partners should have explicit roles, design and approve proactive buy-sell agreements, and clearly separate *equity* in the business from the *salary* a partner is paid to do a job.

"There's a huge difference between ownership and your job within the company. And you need to separate that upfront," he says. "It drives a wedge when there's an inequity in the amount of work done for the salary that is taken. Pay yourself as an *employee*. And if a partner doesn't want to show up for work, pay someone else to do the job. Clearly separate this salary from equity."

Finally, Brett cautions entrepreneurs to be careful about mixing business with friendship or family and the emotions stemming from that arrangement.

"Having someone who you've considered a longtime friend as part of the business has emotion tied to it that is a challenge," he says. "In my case, once money became part of the conversation, the friendship was gone. It's just amazing. It was no longer an objective conversation because of the emotions involved. In retrospect, I try to put myself in his shoes. And I think he felt betrayed when I wanted to leave and do my own thing, as if he was on the bad end of a divorce."

"Handling friendships and partnerships is really, really difficult," he continues. "But I learned some valuable lessons and now love what I do. So, in the end, a lot of things in your life just lead you to where you are."

Acknowledgments

THIS BOOK WAS MADE POSSIBLE by many individuals who encouraged me to tell this story, contributed details to it, or otherwise helped me do it—and I'm immensely grateful for their support. I'm especially thankful for the case study participants who agreed to tell their stories.

Richard Anderson, Dave Sobel, Arlin Sorenson, Dave Cava, Robert Lindley, and Brett Jaffe were all enthusiastically willing to share their experiences and highly candid about the challenges they faced. I am grateful for their participation, honesty, support, and friendship.

My designer, Elena Reznikova, went above and beyond creating a beautiful book, also patiently guiding me through the publication process. Bill Ardolino helped me structure this story and put it into words while providing crucial edits. And I'd like to thank my sister Acacia for reviewing the narrative, prose, and design— and just being there for me during the process. She's long been my invaluable all-around counsel in many aspects of life, and this book is no exception.

Finally, I'd like to thank my clients, colleagues, and fellow entrepreneurs who have gone through the M&A process and provided perspectives that informed the narrative. We've all experienced similar struggles, and I appreciate the hard-won knowledge that may help other small business owners sell successfully.

About the Author

JAMISON WEST has been a serial entrepreneur for 25 years. He founded a managed IT services provider (MSP) that grew from a one-person shop to over 40 employees through both organic growth and the acquisition of four other companies.

After selling the MSP, Jamison went on to co-found three SaaS companies and a business coaching firm. He currently serves as a founder and strategic business coach at ConnectStrat (connectstrat.com), a fractional CEO for SmileBack (smile-back.com), and the Chairman of TimeZest (timezest.com). Business leadership and coaching enable Jamison to leverage his passion for helping others, as he assists entrepreneurs in overcoming challenges to grow their businesses.

Jamison currently lives in Las Vegas, NV.

www.jamisonwest.com

Made in the USA
Columbia, SC
26 October 2021